EVANGELIZATION

AND THE ACTS OF THE APOSTLES

STUDY GUIDE

LECTIO

UNVEILING SCRIPTURE AND TRADITION

DR. MARY HEALY

Nihil Obstat: Dr. André Villeneuve, *Censor Librorum*
Imprimatur: Most Reverend Samuel J. Aquila, S.T.L., Archbishop of Denver
March 2016

Writers: Heather Akers, Ashley Crane, Kris Gray, Therese Obagi

Video Production: Jon Ervin, Steve Flanigan, Justin Leddick, Kevin Mallory, Ted Mast, John Schmidt

Print Production/Graphic Design: Ann Diaz, Brenda Kraft, Jane Myers, Devin Schadt

Augustine Institute
6160 South Syracuse Way, Suite 310
Greenwood Village, CO 80111

For more information: 303-937-4420
Formed.org

Printed in the United States of America
ISBN 978-0-9972037-2-1

(Cover Art) Christ appearing to his disciples at the mount of Galilee / Scala / Art Resource, NY

TABLE OF CONTENTS

EVANGELIZATION
AND THE ACTS OF THE APOSTLES

LECTIO™

UNVEILING SCRIPTURE AND TRADITION

What Is LECTIO?

To read is to discover meaning from written symbols or text. Letters form into words, words into sentences, and sentences into whole paragraphs and pages that communicate our thoughts, teach new ideas, and narrate stories that we find amusing, sorrowful, imaginative, or deeply profound.

The Latin term *lectio* means "reading." The tradition of reading Sacred Scripture for prayer and reflection was practiced by many of the early Church Fathers—St. Ambrose, St. Jerome, St. Augustine, St. Cyprian, and St. John Chrysostom, just to name a few. Benedictine monks later developed this practice into the tradition known as *lectio divina*, or "divine reading."

LECTIO uses the practice of prayerful reading and study to help us dive more deeply into the truths of the faith and discover the profound meaning and purpose of Sacred Scripture, Sacred Tradition, and Church History. We combine engaging sessions led by Catholic teachers with practical guidance for living the faith and developing the disciplines of reading, reflecting, and responding.

By prayerfully reading and understanding the texts of Sacred Scripture and Tradition, we can come to discover the story of salvation into which our Baptism has united us, the history of God's people through the centuries, and the depth of God's love for each of us.

WELCOME TO LECTIO

Welcome to the LECTIO Study Series. In these sessions of LECTIO, you will discover the profound importance, meaning, purpose, and beauty of Sacred Scripture and Sacred Tradition, as seen through the eyes of the Church.

LECTIO studies are designed for Adult Faith Formation to help unveil both Sacred Scripture and Sacred Tradition. The Latin word *lectio* means "reading," and often refers to a careful and prayerful reading of Scripture. These studies cover a wide variety of topics, including individual books or letters of the Bible, the lives and writings of the saints, Church teaching, and topics to help serve the formation of Catholics living out the call of the New Evangelization.

A LECTIO SESSION

This Study Guide takes you step by step through each session, both the small group gathering and video teaching, as well as five days of personal follow-up study. The resources are carefully crafted to lead you through an opening of your heart and mind to God's Word and the traditions of the Catholic Church.

Here is what you will find in each LECTIO session:

CONNECT

1. **Opening Prayer:** For this study on Evangelization, we have chosen the Prayer to the Holy Spirit.

2. **Introduction:** We begin with a brief overview of the topic, including the key points for the session. This helps contextualize the topic, show its relevance for daily life, and inspire you to delve into a particular aspect of the faith.

3. **CONNECT Questions:** After reviewing the verse and daily reflections from the previous session, you'll share your thoughts on questions related to the new session.

VIDEO

4. **Video Teaching:** The video segments present teaching that delves into and makes relevant the Sacred Scripture and Sacred Tradition of the Catholic Church. The video teachings for the study on Evangelization and the Acts of the Apostles are presented by Dr. Mary Healy, Associate Professor of Sacred Scripture at Sacred Heart Major Seminary in Detroit. An outline of each teaching is included in the Study Guide.

DISCUSS

5. **DISCUSS Questions:** Each video segment is followed by questions that will help you personalize and take ownership of the topics of the session.

6. **Memory Verse:** The Psalms encourage us to treasure God's Word in our heart through memorization, saying, "I have laid up thy word in my heart..." (Psalm 119:11). You are encouraged to memorize and reflect on a Scripture verse for every session to help nurture your faith.

7. **Closing Prayer:** The Closing Prayer has been chosen to reflect back to God an appropriate response to his loving action in the session.

8. **For Further Reading:** For supplemental study, you are encouraged to refer to the additional reading resources.

9. **Quotes, Tips, and Definitions:** We have included throughout the study interesting quotes and excerpts from saints, Catholic documents, the *Catechism of the Catholic Church*, and Catholic authors to enhance your understanding of each topic.

COMMIT

The Study Guide includes five daily COMMIT reflections that will help you more deeply explore the main topics of each session and more firmly commit to following Christ in your daily life. These reflections include more information on Sacred Tradition and Sacred Scripture, as well as topics such as geography, history, and art. Some of these reflections will also include times of prayer, including the practice of Scripture meditation known as *lectio divina*.

AN OVERVIEW OF *LECTIO DIVINA*

Lectio divina is an ancient practice of enhancing one's prayer life through the power of God's Word. The term itself means "divine reading" of the Sacred Scriptures. It is our hope that by using these simple steps each day as you study Sacred Scripture in LECTIO, you will develop an effective way to study and pray with God's Word and hear God's voice in your daily life.

- *Sacred Reading of the Scriptures (lectio):* The reading and rereading of the Scripture passage, paying close attention to words, details, themes, and patterns that speak to you.

- *Meditation (meditatio):* Meditating or reflecting on what you've read to gain understanding. Allow the Holy Spirit to guide you as you spend time pondering what you have read and striving to understand it in meditation.

- *Prayer (oratio):* A time to bring your meditative thoughts to God in prayer. Talking with God about how the connections and implications of your meditation on the Scripture affect your life and the lives of those around you.

- *Contemplation (contemplatio):* A time of quiet and rest, we listen and await God's voice. Contemplation allows one to enter decisively and more deeply into the mystery of God—this is no small endeavor, so be patient as you engage this step and strive to be receptive to God's voice speaking into your life.

- *Resolution (resolutio):* A call for resolution and action, inviting you to respond to the things you have read in Scripture and have prayed about, and to put them into practice.

To learn more about *lectio divina*, refer to Dr. Tim Gray's book *Praying Scripture for a Change*, available at www.AscensionPress.com.

SESSION 1

WHY STUDY ACTS?

OPENING PRAYER

Come Holy Spirit,
fill the hearts of your faithful
and enkindle in them
the fire of your love.
Send forth your Spirit
and they shall be created.
And you shall renew the face of the earth.

Let us pray.
O, God, who did instruct
the hearts of the faithful
by the light of the Holy Spirit,
grant that by the same Holy Spirit
we may be truly wise
and ever rejoice in his consolation.
Through Christ our Lord,
Amen.

INTRODUCTION

The Church has been spreading the gospel
for nearly 2,000 years, but people in our
modern world seem to have closed their ears
and hearts to the good news of Jesus Christ.
The "signs of the times" show us a world that
is in desperate need of the gospel, and yet
a "New Evangelization" appears at times to
face insurmountable difficulties. How do we
go about effectively evangelizing the modern
culture in which we find ourselves? Can
stepping back and looking at how the first
Christians turned the ancient world upside
down give us a key for transforming our
modern world? Let's take a look.

Christ appearing to his disciples at the mount of
Galilee / Scala / Art Resource, NY

3

CONNECT

What do you think of when you hear the word "evangelize"?

Do you think that spreading the faith is a priority for the Catholic Church? What about for your parish, specifically?

DISCUSS

PART 1: SIGNS OF THE TIMES
Watch the video teaching. The following is a brief outline of the topics covered.

I. Reading the Signs of the Times
  A. *Gaudium et Spes* (The Church in the Modern World) (Vatican II) calls us to do just this
  B. A "tsunami of secular influence"
    1. Many baptized Christians are no longer living the Christian life
    2. Many are living a "practical atheism," living as if God did not exist
    3. Many hold ideas of God that are alien to Christian faith
    4. This secularism began with Enlightenment, when an outward framework of Christian society remained
    5. But today, no longer a basic consensus in agreement with the gospel
    6. Today, a new militant atheism and attempts to banish God

II. We Live in a Time of Biblical Illiteracy
   A. Biblical worldview helps us make sense
      of history
   B. Biblical worldview helps us make sense
      of our own lives

III. The World Is a Spiritual War Zone
   A. Pope Francis: "The Church is a field hospital"
   B. If a field hospital, then bullets whizzing by
   C. Time has passed for business as usual
   D. Each of us is born for such a time as this

DISCUSS

1. What was one thing you heard for the first time or that was an "aha" moment for you?

_____

_____

_____

2. In what ways have you experienced or witnessed the "tsunami of secularism" mentioned by Cardinal Wuerl? How might this make evangelization difficult?

_____

_____

_____

3. What is the difference between living according to a "practical atheism" and living according to a biblical worldview? What can we do to foster a biblical worldview in ourselves and in others?

_____

_____

_____

PART 2: A BLUEPRINT FOR THE CHURCH
Watch the video teaching. The following is a brief outline of the topics covered.

I. Evangelization Is the Mission of the Church
   A. Pope Bl. Paul VI: "[The Church] exists
      in order to evangelize"
   B. Pope St. John Paul II: Time to commit
      to a New Evangelization
      1. No longer just to those in remote locations
      2. Re-evangelization of Western culture

C. Pope Francis: Each Christian is to be a
   missionary disciple

_____

II. How Have We Been Responding So Far?

_____

  A. Only 30% of baptized American Catholics
     practicing their faith

_____

  B. Fastest growing category is "nones"—
     those who identify as having no religion

_____

  C. Of those who are newly baptized into the
     Church, within a year, half or more stop
     attending Mass regularly

_____

  D. Only 6% of Catholics feel that spreading
     the faith is a high priority

_____

  E. Catholics scored lower than even atheists
     in knowledge of the Bible and Christianity

_____

III. Something More Needs to Happen

_____

  A. Need to look at the First Evangelization

  B. Acts of the Apostles as a blueprint

_____

DISCUSS

4. We are tasked with evangelizing a society that was once largely Christian, but has abandoned the gospel. How is the need for evangelization today both similar to and different from the situation of the first Christians? What particular challenges do you think exist in evangelizing a post-Christian culture?

_____

_____

_____

5. Pope Francis has called for each Christian to be a "missionary disciple." What does this mean? What can you do to live out this call?

_____

_____

_____

PART 3: ACTS OF THE APOSTLES
Watch the video teaching. The following is a brief outline of the topics covered.

I. St. Luke

  A. Author of the Gospel of Luke and
     Acts of the Apostles

_____

  B. Only Gentile author of the New Testament

_____

  C. Acts 16:10: "We" appears; first-person narrative
     showing St. Luke was an eye-witness

_____

    D. Excellent historian, but not a modern historian

    E. Shapes what he writes theologically

II. The Opening of the Acts of the Apostles

    A. Gospel only tells what Jesus
       "began to do and teach"

    B. Jesus continues to act and teach
       through his Church

    C. Repeats Great Commission and the promise
       of the Spirit from end of gospel

    D. Evangelization is first God's work

III. Mary, Model for the Church

    A. Annunciation is a proto-Pentecost

    B. Visitation is the first Christian evangelization

       1. Mary can't keep Jesus to herself

       2. The Spirit is contagious—John leaps and
          Elizabeth is filled with the Spirit

       3. Overflowing praise

IV. We Need a New Pentecost

DISCUSS

6. What does the opening of the Acts of the Apostles teach us about evangelization? How can we apply this to our evangelization efforts today?

_____

_____

_____

7. What are the similarities between the coming of the Holy Spirit in the Acts of the Apostles (Pentecost) and the coming of the Spirit in the gospel (the Annunciation)? How does Mary set a model of evangelization for us?

_____

_____

_____

MEMORY VERSE

"These men who have turned the world upside down."
                                                —Acts 17:6

CLOSING PRAYER

Lord Jesus Christ,
by the power of the Holy Spirit
the first Christians
turned the world upside down
for love of you.
By that same Spirit
may we have the courage
to live lives of missionary discipleship
in order to share the gospel
and transform our world
for the glory of your name.
Amen.

St. Luke, pray for us.

FOR FURTHER READING

Pope St. John Paul II, *Redemptoris Missio (Mission of the Redeemer)*

Joseph Cardinal Ratzinger, Address to Catechists and Religion Teachers, Jubilee of Catechists (December 2000)

Pope Bl. Paul VI, *Evangelii Nuntiandi (Evangelization in the Modern World)*

"Those who with God's help have welcomed Christ's call and freely responded to it are urged on by love of Christ to proclaim the Good News everywhere in the world."
                                                —CCC 3

COMMIT—DAY 1
ST. LUKE

Before studying any literary work, it is helpful to know something about the author. An author's background, credentials, and purpose impact our understanding of what he or she has written. The same is true in studying Scripture. Knowing the author of a particular book of the Bible gives us insight into understanding the work and the way in which it is written.

The Acts of the Apostles is attributed to St. Luke, along with the gospel that bears his name. The book of Acts is clearly written as a sequel to Luke's gospel, as the author begins both works by addressing a specific recipient, Theophilus (see Luke 1:1-3 and Acts 1:1), and Acts is specifically designated to follow the "first book" (Acts 1:1). Luke's gospel ends with Jesus' Resurrection and Ascension; and Acts opens with these same two events. In fact, Jesus' words at the Ascension recorded in Acts 1:8, "But you shall

St Luke the Evangelist writing his Gospel watched by his symbol, an ox / HIP / Art Resource, NY

receive power when the Holy Spirit has come upon you; and you shall be my witnesses in Jerusalem and in all Judea and Samaria and to the end of the earth," provide the structure for the rest of the book. Acts 1–7 describes Jesus' Ascension, the Apostles' reception of the Holy Spirit at Pentecost, and their immediate preaching in Jerusalem; chapters 8–12 describe the gospel spreading to Judea and Samaria; and in chapters 13–28 Christianity begins its spread to the rest of the Roman world, whose empire stretched to the reaches of the known world.

The story of Acts concludes with St. Paul being placed under house arrest in Rome. Interestingly, St. Luke doesn't include major events of the following years in the Acts of the Apostles—events such as the Great Fire of Rome in 64 AD; Nero's persecution of the Christians, including the martyrdoms of Sts. Peter and Paul, following thereafter; and the conquest of Jerusalem and destruction of the Temple in 70 AD. Perhaps Luke had already written Acts by that time; or perhaps Paul's arrival at Rome, the capital city of the Roman empire, where Paul was "preaching the kingdom of God and teaching about the Lord Jesus Christ quite openly" (Acts 28:31), provided the matching bookend to Jesus' opening words in Acts 1:8, showing that the gospel had indeed spread to the ends of the earth. Regardless of Luke's reason for concluding as he does, his open ending of Acts moves us right into the rest of the history of the Church that follows the Apostolic Age.

St. Luke was a Gentile, and the only non-Jewish author of a New Testament book. Luke mixes the best of Hebrew and Greek styles of history in his writing. Like the Hebrew authors of the Old Testament, Luke records the theological sense of history as he shows how God is the author of all history and the power behind the events narrated in Acts. Thus, for example, Luke records the angel of God setting free the Apostles (see Acts 5), and later St. Peter (see Acts 12), from jail. Like his contemporary Greek writers, Luke also focuses on the moral lessons contained in the history of the early years of the Church. The very title of his second work, "Acts" takes its name from an ancient Greek literary genre focused on studying the deeds and acts—*praxis* in Greek—of great men so that these deeds were not forgotten and that others might imitate them and, in

Saint Luke the Evangelist, about to write the Gospel / Alfredo Dagli Orti / Art Resource, NY

doing so, build up human civilization. In writing his account as an "Acts" or *praxis*, Luke is inviting his Christian audience to imitate the virtuous lives of the Apostles, who in turn are imitating Christ himself, not simply to build up human civilization, but to build up the Kingdom of God.

By occupation St. Luke was a physician (see Colossians 4:14). After his conversion, Luke accompanied St. Paul on some of his journeys. In Acts 16:10, Luke switches his narrative from the third person to the first person. His use of "we" and "us," here and in other passages, indicates that Luke was an eyewitness to many of the events he records in the Acts of the Apostles.

Look up Acts 16:10–17; 20:5–21:18; and 27:1–28:16. What are some of the events St. Luke witnessed or participated in? Why is Luke's status as an eyewitness important to our understanding of Acts?

_____

_____

_____

Piecing together Acts of the Apostles and the letters of St. Paul, we get a fuller picture of St. Luke's ministry. Luke remained in Philippi when Paul departed (Acts 16:40), most likely to continue preaching the gospel in that city. According to Philippians 4:15-16, the church at Philippi sent Paul monetary aid while he was in Thessalonica, and Luke probably arranged this support. Paul met Luke again when he returned to Philippi. Paul wrote his second letter to the Corinthians during this visit to Philippi, and according to St. Jerome, the "brother" mentioned in 2 Corinthians 8:18 is Luke, and Luke was one of the messengers who took Paul's letter back to Corinth. Luke returned to Jerusalem with Paul and remained with him through Paul's two-year imprisonment in Caesarea and his journey to Rome. Luke was present with Paul in Rome for at least part of his first imprisonment there, as he is mentioned in two of the three letters Paul wrote during that time (Colossians 4:14 and Philemon 1:24, but not in the letter to the Ephesians). Luke was also at Paul's side for his last imprisonment, as Paul states in 2 Timothy 4:7-11. Not much is known about Luke's life after the martyrdom of Paul. One ancient historian (Epiphanius) writes that he preached in Dalmatia, Gallia (or Galatia), Italy, and Macedonia. An ancient tradition says Luke died in Boeotia in Greece at 84 years old, unmarried and "full of the Holy Spirit."

St. Luke / Smithsonian American Art Museum, Washington, DC / Art Resource, NY

St. Luke is the patron saint of doctors, being a physician himself. An ancient tradition holds that he painted several pictures (icons) of the Virgin Mary and child Jesus, including the Salus Populi Romani preserved in the Basilica of St. Mary Major in Rome. Because of this Luke is considered the father of Christian iconography and is the patron saint of painters. Drawing from the traditional symbols of the four gospel writers (described in Revelation 4:6-7—man, lion, ox, eagle), Luke is often represented by the ox, since he opens his gospel with the priest Zechariah in the Temple, and cattle were among the animals used for Temple sacrifice. St. Luke's feast day is celebrated on October 18.

COMMIT—DAY 2
SIGNS OF THE TIMES

"The Church has always had the duty of scrutinizing the signs of the times and of interpreting them in the light of the Gospel. Thus, in language intelligible to each generation, she can respond to the perennial questions which men ask about this present life and the life to come, and about the relationship of the one to the other. We must therefore recognize and understand the world in which we live, its explanations, its longings, and its often dramatic characteristics."

—*Gaudium et Spes*, 4

The Second Vatican Council reaffirmed the Church's duty to read the signs of the times, not in order to conform to those times, as so many would have the Church do, but to better address the gospel message "in language intelligible to each generation." In order to share the good news of Jesus Christ in a way that is relevant and inviting, we must know our audience—what are they searching for? What are their needs and fears? In order to show each new generation how the gospel answers such questions, we must read the signs of the times.

The signs of the our current times reveal a world that hasn't simply turned away from Christianity, but one that has also turned toward secularism, relativism, and hedonism. In shutting God out of the picture, a vacuum opens up that must be filled with something. As the lyrics of one Bob Dylan song reminds:

"But you're gonna have to serve somebody, yes indeed.
You're gonna have to serve somebody.
It may be the devil or it may be the Lord,
But you're gonna have to serve somebody."

In abandoning a biblical worldview, modern society has opened itself up to a wide variety of alternatives. What are some of the secular worldviews you have encountered in your interactions with others? How have such interactions impacted your life?

_____

_____

In many parts of the world today, Christians are experiencing intense persecution and even martyrdom—a fact that is often largely ignored by secular society. In the West this persecution is more subtle. As secularism gains power, Christians are expected to practice their faith in private and live their public lives according to rules of political correctness and "tolerance." Letting one's faith inform one's business decisions or political activity is often seen as forcing one's faith on others, rather than as a right to be protected. The signs of the times point to a world increasingly hostile to the Church. Have you or someone you know experienced persecution for your faith? What happened? How did you respond?

_____

_____

The signs of the times also point to some causes of concern within the Church as well. Low participation in Mass and the sacraments, and a lack of understanding about even the Church's most basic teachings, are all too common among men and women who identify as Catholic.

Jonah and the Whale, drawings by Gustave Dore © Nicku / shutterstock.com

As dark as these times seem, this isn't the first time in history that God's people have faced difficulties arising from a world in desperate need of conversion. Consider the story of Jonah. In the mid-8th century BC, the Northern Kingdom of Israel was facing threats from the neighboring Assyrian Empire. God called Jonah to travel deep into enemy territory to the Assyrian city of Nineveh and call the people of the city to repentance. Jonah didn't want anything to do with this mission to Israel's enemies and took off in the opposite direction. After a storm at sea followed by three days of darkness, distress and anguish in the belly of the great fish, God heard Jonah's prayer and gave him a second chance. He went to Nineveh and walked the city streets, warning the people that God would destroy their city if they didn't repent of their sins and change their ways. Then he set up camp outside the city to watch the impending destruction of his people's wicked enemies. But Jonah was in for a surprise. The people of Nineveh heeded his message. They turned away from their wickedness, and God spared them, pouring out his mercy and bringing about a conversion of Israel's enemy.

Scripture also gives us examples of internal reform and conversion of God's people during the reigns of two kings of the Southern Kingdom of Judah, Hezekiah (2 Chronicles 29:31) and Josiah (2 Chronicle 34). Both kings, Hezekiah starting in the late 8th century BC, and Josiah three generations later, were faithful men of God in the midst of a nation that had largely turned away from God and forsaken his commandments. Both Hezekiah and Josiah worked to eradicate idolatry and renew the liturgical life of God's people centered on the Temple in Jerusalem. They repaired the Temple, renewed the nation's dedication to God's Law, and lived lives of faithfulness and trust in God. Although both Hezekiah and Josiah ascended the throne of a kingdom wandering far from God, both kings enacted radical reforms and under their rule Judah was once again faithful and enjoyed God's favor.

How do the stories of Jonah, Hezekiah, and Josiah apply to our own times? What encouragement and lessons can we draw from these stories?

_____

_____

_____

Jesus Preaches in the Synagogue, drawings by Gustave Dore. © Nicku / shutterstock.com

The times in which we find ourselves call for both our own deeper conversion and fidelity to Jesus Christ and his Church, as well as a creativity to apply the truth of the gospel to the questions asked by the men and women of the culture around us. As Dr. Healy shared in the video, the New Evangelization is still about proclaiming the gospel to those who have never heard it, but ever more often it is proclaiming the gospel to those who think they already know it and have rejected it. As Venerable Fulton Sheen famously said, "There are not one hundred people in the United States who hate the Catholic Church, but there are millions who hate what they wrongly perceive the Catholic Church to be." For a New Evangelization to be successful, we must allow the Spirit to fill us with a new vigor and zeal for sharing the good news of Jesus Christ. We must be willing to explore new methods of sharing the gospel, and we must share it with a new and fresh expression so that our jaded, post-Christian world will open their ears and their hearts.

COMMIT—DAY 3
LECTIO: THE VISITATION

St. Luke includes a beautiful symmetry between the beginning of his gospel and the beginning of the Acts of the Apostles. Both books begin with a coming of the Holy Spirit followed by an act of evangelization—sharing the love of God communicated by the Holy Spirit. Reading and praying through Mary's visitation to her cousin Elizabeth allows us the opportunity to meditate on the first act of Christian evangelization and sheds light on our own call to share the good news of Jesus Christ with others.

> **LECTIO:** The practice of praying with Scripture, *lectio divina*, begins with an active and close reading of the Scripture passage. Read the Scripture passage below and then answer the questions to take a closer look at some of the details of the passage.

"In those days Mary arose and went with haste into the hill country, to a city of Judah, and she entered the house of Zechariah and greeted Elizabeth. And when Elizabeth heard the greeting of Mary, the child leaped in her womb; and Elizabeth was filled with the Holy Spirit and she exclaimed with a loud cry, 'Blessed are you among women, and blessed is the fruit of your womb! And why is this granted me, that the mother of my Lord should come to me? For behold, when the voice of your greeting came to my ears, the child in my womb leaped for joy. And blessed is she who believed there would be a fulfilment of what was spoken to her from the Lord.' And Mary said,

'My soul magnifies the Lord,
and my spirit rejoices in God my Savior,
for he has regarded the low estate of his handmaiden.
For behold, henceforth all generations will call me blessed;
for he who is mighty has done great things for me,
and holy is his name.
And his mercy is on those who fear him
from generation to generation.
He has shown strength with his arm,
he has scattered the proud in the imagination of their hearts,
he has put down the mighty from their thrones
and exalted those of low degree;
he has filled the hungry with good things,
and the rich he has sent empty away.
He has helped his servant Israel,
in remembrance of his mercy,
as he spoke to our fathers,
to Abraham and to his posterity for ever.'
And Mary remained with her about three months, and returned to her home."

—Luke 1:39–56

Visitation of the Blessed Virgin Mary
© *Zvonimir Atletic / shuterstock.com*

What actions does Mary perform in this passage? What does Elizabeth do? What does the child (John the Baptist) do?

_____

_____

What are Elizabeth and John's reactions to Mary's arrival? What emotions does Mary express?

_____

_____

What are the themes of Mary's Magnificat (verses 46–55)?

_____

_____

MEDITATIO: *Lectio*, close reading and rereading, is followed by *meditatio*, time to reflect on the Scripture passage, to ponder the reason for particular events, descriptions, details, phrases, and even echoes from other Scripture passages that were noticed during *lectio*. Take some time now to meditate on the Scripture passage on page 15.

The following meditation is taken from Pope Benedict XVI's Address at the Conclusion of the Marian Month, May 31, 2008:

"*Let us imagine the Virgin's state of mind after the Annunciation, when the Angel left her. Mary found herself with a great mystery enclosed within her womb; she knew something extraordinarily unique had happened; she was aware that the last chapter of salvation history in the world had begun. But everything around her remained as before and the village of Nazareth was completely unaware of what had happened to her.*

"*Before worrying about herself, Mary instead thought about elderly Elizabeth, who she knew was well on in her pregnancy and, moved by the mystery of love that she had just welcomed within herself, she set out 'in haste' to go to offer Elizabeth her help. This is the simple and sublime greatness of Mary!*

"*When she reaches Elizabeth's house, an event takes place that no artist could ever portray with the beauty and the intensity with which it took place. The interior light of the Holy Spirit enfolds their persons. And Elizabeth, enlightened from on high, exclaims: 'Blessed are you among women, and blessed is the fruit of your womb! ...'*"

Visitation of the Virgin and Saint Elizabeth / Scala/Ministero per i Beni e le Attività culturali / Art Resource, NY

Consider the actions of each person in this passage. How is each action an appropriate response to the presence of the Holy Spirit? How do these actions present a model for evangelization?

_____

_____

With whom do you identify most closely in this passage? Why?

_____

_____

Our emotions often play a key role in our lives of faith. When has your response or reaction to the Holy Spirit been similar to that of Elizabeth or John? When has it been similar to the response of Mary?

_____

_____

Which themes of Mary's Magnificat resonate most with you? Why? If you were to write your own Magnificat modeled on Mary's, what would it include?

_____

_____

ORATIO, CONTEMPLATIO, RESOLUTIO: Having read and meditated on today's Scripture passage, take some time to bring your thoughts to God (*oratio*) and engage God in silence (*contemplatio*). Then end your prayer by making a simple concrete resolution (*resolutio*) to respond to God's prompting of your heart in today's prayer.

_____

_____

_____

Technology in the hands of businessmen
© violetkaipa / shutterstock.com

We live in a world of constant activity. Modern technology allows us to do more than ever. Smartphones and tablets allow us to constantly be in touch, working, and *doing* something. And society pushes us to take full advantage of every opportunity to be more productive, accomplish more, and fit even more into our already hectic lives.

In the midst of all of this busyness, waiting seems like a foreign concept and doesn't come easily to most of us. When there is a dream or a goal in sight, it can be downright painful to wait for God's timing rather than pursuing it on our own schedule. Additionally, when we are called to begin our work in prayer it can seem, by the standards of the world, that we are simply wasting time without accomplishing anything. But God's plan is always worth the wait.

When have you tried to do something on your own rather than waiting for God? When have you waited for God's timing?

_____

_____

The story of the Church begins with waiting. Jesus' instruction to his Apostles before his Ascension to remain in Jerusalem and "wait for the promise of the Father" (Acts 1:4) almost seems to interrupt the momentum of the story. Jesus has risen from the dead and is preparing to ascend to the right hand of the Father. The New Covenant has been ratified, and the world is ripe for the message of the gospel. And yet the Apostles are told to wait.

The Pentecost / Scala / Art Resource, NY

The Apostles respond to this command to wait by asking what Jesus is going to do—will he now restore the kingdom to Israel? Jesus does not answer their question with "times or seasons." Instead Jesus announces that the Apostles are to be his witnesses, but only after they receive the power of the Holy Spirit. And so they wait. And they pray. And in due time Jesus sends the Holy Spirit upon his followers. Filled with this power from on high, their witness is such that they turn "the world upside down" (Acts 17:6). The Apostles could not have accomplished the evangelization of the ancient world simply with their own power or in their own time. It could only be done by the power of the Holy Spirit and according to his schedule. Rather than interrupting the momentum of this first evangelization, waiting and praying gave them the grace and strength that turned the world upside down.

"But they who wait for the LORD shall renew their strength, they shall mount up with wings like eagles, they shall run and not be weary, they shall walk and not faint." —Isaiah 40:31

If Jesus' first instruction for the first evangelization was to wait for the Spirit, then the same holds true for evangelization in our time. Both the promise and the precedent of Scripture are clear. By the power of the Holy Spirit and according to God's timing, ordinary people can accomplish great things for the Kingdom—just like Jonah, Hezekiah, and Josiah did. Trusting in human effort alone can have disastrous results. Look up Numbers 14:39–45 for an example of the Israelites trying to do something on their own power after God told them to wait. What happened?

_____

The lives of the saints also provide wonderful examples of the power of waiting on God's timing and the Holy Spirit. St. Monica, for one, is an excellent model of waiting on the Lord and persevering in prayer. By worldly standards her life was not one of great accomplishments, but thirty-three years of relentless prayer resulted in her spiritual legacy: the conversion of her son, St. Augustine, who was Bishop of Hippo and writer of numerous treatises on the faith, and who today is considered one of the most important early Church Fathers.

The Bible and the lives of the saints show us that God calls people from all walks of life to accomplish his will. The Old Testament prophets came from a variety of backgrounds: aristocracy, scribes, priests, and farmers. The first pope started out as a fisherman. The Church's history is full of slaves and royalty, scholars and uneducated commoners, skilled craftsmen and simple children who all answered God's call to holiness. There is a saying, "God doesn't call the equipped, he equips the called." An important part of this equipping comes from waiting on the Lord in prayer. The more we unite ourselves to God and his will in prayer, the more open we will find ourselves to the direction of the Holy Spirit.

This is one of the beautiful things about the New Evangelization. We are each called to participate by virtue of our Baptism, but we don't have to rely on our own strengths, or fear our own weaknesses. Just as the first evangelization was accomplished only after the Apostles heeded Jesus' instruction to wait for the Holy Spirit, we also must wait and pray to allow God to inspire and direct our work. Waiting and prayer does not put off evangelization; rather it fuels our love of God and inflames our willingness to share the love we have encountered.

> *"Finally, the person who has been evangelized goes on to evangelize others. Here lies the test of truth, the touchstone of evangelization: it is unthinkable that a person should accept the Word and give himself to the kingdom without becoming a person who bears witness to it and proclaims it in his turn."* —Pope Bl. Paul VI, *Evangelii Nuntiandi*, 24

The world needs to hear the gospel, and if we ask Jesus, "When will you bring about conversion in the world?" he will tell us, just as he told the Apostles, "You will be my witnesses."

In what areas of your life do you feel well-equipped to answer God's call to bear witness to him? In what areas do you feel inadequate? Which Bible stories or saints inspire you as you discern how to give witness to God and his love and work in your life?

_____

_____

The Annunciation, Sandro Botticelli, 1489-90

The Annunciation / Alfredo Dagli Orti / The Art Archive at Art Resource, NY

The Second Vatican Council, repeating the words of St. Ambrose, reminds us, "The Mother of God is a type of the Church in the order of faith, charity and perfect union with Christ" (*Lumen Gentium*, 63). This union is nowhere more wonderfully pictured than at the moment of the Annunciation, when "Mary entrusted herself to God completely, with the 'full submission of intellect and will,' manifesting 'the obedience of faith' to him who spoke to her through his messenger....This response of faith included both perfect cooperation with 'the grace of God that precedes and assists' and perfect openness to the action of the Holy Spirit, who 'constantly brings faith to completion by his gifts'" (Pope St. John Paul II, *Redemptoris Mater*, 13).

The moment of this extraordinary encounter has filled the imagination of artists throughout the centuries, making the Annunciation one of the most frequent subjects of Christian art. One such work was commissioned in May 1489 to be placed in a family chapel in the church of Cestello (now known as Santa Maria Maddalena dei Pazzi) in Florence, Italy. The artist was Sandro Botticelli, an Italian painter from the Florentine school during the Early Renaissance. By the time Botticelli produced this Annunciation scene, he had become a recognized artist, having painted numerous altarpieces as well as contributing to the frescoed walls of the Sistine Chapel. Botticelli's *Annunciation*, sometimes referred to as the *Cestello Annunciation*, now resides in the Uffizi Gallery in Florence.

Botticelli sets the scene, not in the humble surroundings of a Palestinian home in Nazareth, but rather in a room Botticelli himself might have encountered in any nobleman's home in the city of Florence. The pale lines in the terra cotta floor make use of linear perspective to direct our gaze past the protagonists in the foreground, and out the open rear door of the room. Here we look past a small white-walled garden area, barren, in which nothing grows, and out onto a rich green landscape with a river running toward the horizon. Centered in the door's prospect is a slender tree. The view is not unlike what any noble Florentine might have seen looking out his own window onto the Italian countryside, but its simple elements—a garden, a river, and a tree—call to mind the story of Creation and the Garden of Eden, from which flowed several rivers and in which stood the Tree of Life, whose fruit was never tasted.

The stillness of the landscape stands in stark contrast to the graceful movement that appears in the figures of the Angel Gabriel and Mary. Barely visible on the left is the corniced edge of a second doorway, which not only provides a second source of light for Botticelli, who was known for his subtle coloring, but also provides the opening through which the heavenly visitor has just entered, a small portion of his robes still extending out the doorway and beyond our sight.

The centerline of the floor's grid marks an invisible threshold that separates the angelic messenger on the left and the young virgin on the right, and in some sense marks the divide between heaven and earth. Take a look at the painting. Who crosses this line into the other's space?

_____

Gabriel does not remain at the doorway's entrance to the room, but presents himself as close as possible to the center threshold, extending his hand across the threshold and toward Mary. His proximity and his leaning toward her who he has just announced as being "full of grace" acts as an earnest plea for Mary to say "yes" to the incredible plan of God which he has come to announce.

Read Luke 1:29. How does St. Luke describe Mary's response to Gabriel's greeting?

_____

Botticelli seems to use the movement of Mary's body to express the dialogue of the scene. The lower portion of her body gracefully bends away from the angel and his troubling greeting. But as the angel continues revealing God's plan (the key verse of which is recorded in the painting's original architectural-style frame: "The Holy Ghost shall come upon thee, and the power of the Highest shall over shadow thee") and answering her questions, Mary's heart, already given entirely to God from her childhood, overflows with the desire to take her place more and more deeply in God's plan. As if to image her fiat, her "yes," Botticelli gracefully extends Mary's upper body, arms, and hands toward Gabriel.

The Annunciation / Alfredo Dagli Orti / The Art Archive at Art Resource, NY

But while the hands of Gabriel and Mary extend toward each other, they never touch, mirroring the virginal conception of the Incarnation that is about to take place in Mary's womb without the natural physical touch of husband and wife. The extended arms of Gabriel and Mary mark a diagonal across the painting. This first diagonal is intersected by a second that follows the branch of lilies Gabriel holds in his left hand— these beautiful white flowers a symbol Mary's purity.

In contrast to the barren garden visible in the picture's background, the pure virgin's womb will not be barren, but her "yes" to God's plan yields a supernatural fertility and fruitfulness when the Holy Spirit overshadows her. This divine fruit of Mary's womb, Jesus Christ, the Son of God, will undo the curse that exiled mankind from the Garden of Eden. The wood of his Cross will become a new tree of life, the water and blood flowing from his side will become the new river of life in Baptism and the new fruit given in the gift of the Eucharist.

When Mary gives her "yes" to God at the Annunciation, she could not fully see the joys and sorrows ahead, but "she will let herself be led by the hand by mysterious Providence and for her whole life, rooted in faith, she will follow her Son spiritually, becoming his first and perfect 'disciple' and carrying-out in everyday life the requirements involved in following Jesus according to his own words: 'Whoever does not bear his own cross and come after me, cannot be my disciple' (Luke 14:27)" (Pope St. John Paul II, Address at the Conclusion of the Marian Month, May 31, 1979). May we model her faith, charity, and union with Christ, and so also become perfect disciples.

SESSION 2

CLOTHED WITH POWER

OPENING PRAYER

Come Holy Spirit,
fill the hearts of your faithful
and enkindle in them the fire of your love.
Send forth your Spirit
and they shall be created.
And you shall renew the face of the earth.

Let us pray.
O, God, who did instruct
the hearts of the faithful
by the light of the Holy Spirit,
grant that by the same Holy Spirit
we may be truly wise
and ever rejoice in his consolation.
Through Christ our Lord,
Amen.

Mary, Mother of the Church, pray for us.

INTRODUCTION

Think of a great achievement in your life. What was the driving force behind your success? In the first session we began to look at the Acts of the Apostles as a pattern for evangelization. Dr. Healy suggested that the key to modeling the New Evangelization on the first evangelization is to rely on the same power that transformed the ancient world. The first evangelization began only once the disciples were "clothed with power from on high" (Luke 24:49) at Pentecost. With the descent of the Holy Spirit, the Church was born, the Apostles were anointed for their mission, and the world was changed forever. Let's take a closer look at this gift of the Holy Spirit at Pentecost, which was the driving force of the first evangelization's success, and rediscover the power of the Spirit in our own lives so that we can be effective witnesses to Jesus Christ.

CONNECT

When were you baptized? Confirmed? What do you remember about your reception of these sacraments?

What do you think it means to be baptized in the Holy Spirit?

DISCUSS

> **PART 1: BAPTIZED WITH THE HOLY SPIRIT**
> *Watch the teaching on video. The following is a brief outline of the topics covered.*

I. "Baptized with the Holy Spirit" (Acts 1:4-5)
   A. Phrase appears in all four gospels and in Acts _____
   B. Baptize: to immerse/dip/plunge in water _____
   C. St. John's baptism was a cleansing of sin _____
   D. The baptism of Jesus was key for his mission _____
   E. Pentecost is key for the mission of the Church _____
   F. Our Baptism is key for our mission as Christians _____

II. Jesus' Baptism
   A. Jesus is anointed/baptized with the Holy Spirit _____
   B. The Spirit allows Jesus, in his human nature,
      to resist evil _____
   C. First sermon summarizes his mission:
      to proclaim good news (Isaiah 61:1-2) _____

D. *"This is why we are called Christians:*
   because we are anointed with the oil of God"
         —Theophilus of Antioch

III. Coming of the Kingdom
   A. "You shall receive power when the
      Holy Spirit has come upon you" —Acts 1:8
   B. The kingdom will come through the
      apostolic work of evangelization
   C. Ever-widening circles: Jerusalem, Judea
      and Samaria, end of the earth

IV. Jesus' Ascension
   A. "A cloud took him"—recalls Exodus and
      Mount Sinai
   B. "Two men stood by them"—possibly Moses
      and Elijah
      1. From Moses, Joshua receives the spirit
         to lead God's people
      2. From Elijah, Elisha receives double
         portion of his spirit

DISCUSS

1. What was one thing you heard for the first time or that was an "aha" moment for you?

_____

_____

2. What do Jesus' words and actions after his baptism tell us about the effects and purpose of being anointed with the Spirit?

_____

_____

3. How are we made "little christs," as Dr. Healy calls us? What does it mean? What implications does it have for our lives and efforts at evangelization?

_____

_____

PART 2: PENTECOST AND THE UPPER ROOM
Watch the video teaching. The following is a brief outline of the topics covered.

I.   Upper Room Is a Room of Resurrection in Acts

II. Church Gathered for Pentecost
     A. All devoted to prayer
     B. One accord—expresses unity in body of Christ
     C. St. Luke mentions Mary's presence; she first
        received the Spirit at Annunciation
     D. List of Apostles
        1. Twelve chosen, but Judas is missing
        2. Why is Judas replaced?
        3. Once the Spirit comes, God's people can
           be expanded
        4. Apostle chosen by lots—priestly leadership

III. Pentecost (Feast of Weeks)
     A. Feast celebrating the gift of the Law
     B. Audio and visual phenomena recall
        theophany on Mount Sinai
     C. St. Paul best explains what it means to be
        "filled with the Holy Spirit"
        1. Revelation of the Father's love
           (Romans 5:5)
        2. Revelation of the Lordship of Jesus
           (1 Corinthians 12:3)

IV. St. Luke Shows Us the Outward Effects
     A. Overflowing praise of God and proclaiming
        the good news
     B. St. Peter rebuked and denied Jesus before,
        now proclaims Jesus unafraid
     C. Nationalities in the crowd:
        1. Egypt—enslaved God's people
        2. Mesopotamia—Assyrians and Babylonians
           took God's people into exile
        3. Isaiah 19:23-25—"In that day..."
     D. People hear in their own language:
        reversal of the Tower of Babel (Genesis 11);
        uniting power of the Holy Spirit

DISCUSS

4. What does it mean to be filled with the Holy Spirit? Have you ever experienced this?

_____

_____

5. How have you witnessed the transformative power of the Holy Spirit in your own life? In the lives of others?

_____

_____

PART 3: SOBER INTOXICATION OF THE SPIRIT
Watch the video teaching. The following is a brief outline of the topics covered.

I. Signs Don't Force Faith

II. Crowd Thinks Disciples Are Drunk   _____
    A. Wine—refers to abundance of life (Amos 9:13)
    B. New wine is Holy Spirit;   _____

III. Sober Intoxication   _____
    A. St. Cyril of Jerusalem—"sober intoxication
       of the Spirit"   _____
    B. St. Augustine—"May he truly intoxicate you"   _____
    C. Benedict XVI—"Let us rediscover . . . the beauty
       of being baptized in the Holy Spirit"   _____

DISCUSS

6. What signs have you witnessed or experienced that have invited you deeper into your faith?

_____

_____

7. Why do our hearts need to be made new to receive the new life of the Spirit? How are our hearts made new?

_____

_____

MEMORY VERSE

"But you shall receive power when the Holy Spirit has come upon you; and you shall be my witnesses in Jerusalem and in all Judea and Samaria and to the end of the earth."

—Acts 1:8

CLOSING PRAYER

Almighty God,
you clothe your faithful
with the power of your Holy Spirit,
that we may witness to your love and glory
in all that we do.
May we be ever mindful of the gift
of your Spirit,
and in your power resist evil
and proclaim the gospel
through our words and deeds.
We ask this in the name of your Son,
our Lord Jesus Christ.
Amen.

Mary, Mother of the Church, pray for us.

Pentecost. From the doors of the Silver Cabinet. @ Nicolo Orsi Battaglini / Art Resource, NY

FOR FURTHER READING

CCC 731, 1287, 1303

Pope Leo XIII, *Divinum Illud Munus (On the Holy Spirit)*

Pope St. John Paul II, *Dominum et Vivificantem (On the Holy Spirit in the Life of the Church and the World)*

COMMIT—DAY 1
BAPTISM

What do you think of when you hear the word *baptism*? Maybe water, oil, candles, white garments, a church? We might tend to think of baptism as originating with Christianity, but St. John the Baptist's call to repent and be baptized had a precedent in the Jewish law. The Torah specified rituals of washing and sprinkling with water to purify those who had made themselves ritually unclean (see, for example, Numbers 19:18-19). As Dr. Healy stated in the video teaching, the Greek word from which we get baptism was originally a common word that could mean either a simple washing or a ritual purification.

St. John's baptism was a preparation, a type—something that pointed forward to a greater reality in Christ. St. John himself said, "He who is coming after me is mightier than I...he will baptize you with the Holy Spirit and with fire" (Matthew 3:11). When Jesus was baptized by John, he blessed the waters of Baptism and instituted something greater than what John had been offering. John offered a symbol; Jesus gave us a sacrament. Because of Christ, the waters of Baptism effect what they signify: the Sacrament of Baptism cleanses us from sin and causes us to be reborn as children of God. Baptism conforms us to Christ.

Baptismal site at Jordan river shore. Israel. © Oleg Zaslavsky / shutterstock.com

> *"The Lord was baptized, not to be cleansed himself but to cleanse the waters, so that those waters, cleansed by the flesh of Christ which knew no sin, might have the power of Baptism."*
> —St. Ambrose of Milan

Jesus' baptism in the Jordan proclaimed three essential points. First, in going down into the waters of St. John's baptism of repentance, Jesus identified himself with sinners. Although he had no sin, in the Jordan River, he placed himself in the position of sinful humanity. As the *Catechism of the Catholic Church* says, "The baptism of Jesus is on his part the acceptance and inauguration of his mission as God's suffering Servant. He allows himself to be numbered among sinners; he is already 'the Lamb of God, who takes away the sin of the world'....The Spirit whom Jesus possessed in fullness from his conception comes to 'rest on him.' Jesus will be the source of the Spirit for all mankind" (CCC 536). This is what his ministry was to be all about: going to those most in need, meeting them where they were, and lifting them out of their oppression.

Second, the gospels record that at Jesus' baptism a voice from Heaven was heard saying, "This is my beloved Son" (Matthew 3:17). Jesus' identity as the Son of the Father, the Son of God, God himself, was reaffirmed. And third, when the Holy Spirit descended upon him, Jesus' identity as the Messiah, the Christ, the Anointed One, was announced. Jesus is the long awaited Messiah who will save God's people, and all humanity, and as the Son of God he has the power to redeem us from our sin. Having identified himself with sinners and received the anointing of the Spirit, Jesus Christ, the Son of God, immediately set out to begin his ministry.

Take a few minutes to pray the first Luminous Mystery of the Rosary, Jesus' Baptism in the Jordan, reflecting on these three points.

Jesus baptized / © Balage Balogh / Art Resource, NY

Jesus' mission can be described as consisting of three roles: priest, prophet, and king. Christ is our eternal high priest, who offered himself as the perfect sacrifice to the Father (see Hebrews 7:26–8:2). Jesus is the full revelation of God, and as such he is the most perfect prophet—one who reveals God's Word and plan for salvation (see John 1:14, 18). And Jesus is the King of kings and Lord of lords, whose kingdom will encompass all nations and will have no end (see Luke 1:33, Revelation 19:16).

This mission did not come to an end when Jesus ascended into Heaven. As we saw in the last session, St. Luke's gospel gives an account only of what Jesus *"began to do and teach"* (Acts 1:1, emphasis added). The Acts of the Apostles continues the story, not as an account of what the Apostles did in and of themselves, but as an account of the continuation of Christ's actions and teachings through his Church. At Pentecost the Apostles are anointed with the same Spirit with which Christ was anointed—this anointing is the key to the mission of the Church, just as Christ's anointing at his baptism was key to his mission.

Through our Baptism we share in Christ's mission as priest, prophet, and king. Baptism makes us a part of the priesthood of all believers (see 1 Peter 2:5), and as priests we are called to offer sacrifice, to offer ourselves daily as a spiritual sacrifice to God—striving for holiness and mastering the power of sin in our lives—and to offer our worship to God through the Mass, the sacraments, and daily prayer. All the baptized are called to be prophets by sharing the revelation of Christ with the world through evangelization and teaching. And by virtue of our Baptism we are called to reign with Jesus as kings, living out a servant leadership in imitation of our King who came not to be served, but to serve.

"The God of power
and Father of our Lord Jesus Christ
has freed you from sin,
given you a new birth by water
and the Holy Spirit,
and welcomed you into his holy people.
He now anoints you
with the chrism of salvation.
As Christ was anointed Priest, Prophet, and King,
so may you live always as a member of his body,
sharing everlasting life.
Amen."

—From the Rite of Baptism

Baptism. Panel from the campanile / Scala / Art Resource, NY

Our Baptism conforms us to Christ, and by it we participate in Christ's threefold mission of priest, prophet, and king. Our life, our ministry, and our evangelization must also be conformed to Jesus and his mission. What do you think evangelization fully conformed to the mission of Christ looks like? How does our anointing in Baptism shape us for evangelization?

_____

_____

_____

COMMIT–DAY 2
PENTECOST

Take a minute to think about your favorite holidays and everything that makes them special to you. What makes these days stand out from other celebrations during the year?

_____

_____

What about Law Day—did it make your list? Probably not. As admirable as it might be to set aside a day (May 1st, in the United States of America, in case you were wondering) to recognize the liberties protected by our laws, it's just not as exciting as Christmas or Easter.

Moses with the Tablets of the Law / Alinari / Art Resource, NY

For the Israelites, on the other hand, the day set aside to commemorate God's Law, the Torah, was one of the most important feasts each year. This feast is known by several names. It was originally called the Feast of Weeks (Deuteronomy 16:10) or the Feast of Harvest (Exodus 23:16), and it started out as a liturgical celebration to give praise and thanks to God for the spring harvest. Greek-speaking Jews gave it the name of Pentecost, which comes from the Greek word for "fiftieth" and refers to the festival's timing, which occurred fifty days after the Passover celebration (Leviticus 23:15-16). The feast of Pentecost became a time to celebrate God's gift of the law, the Torah, at Mount Sinai, because the timing of the feast on the fiftieth day after Passover matches up with the giving of the law, as according to Exodus 19:1 the law was given fifty days after the first Passover and the departure from Egypt.

Pentecost was much more than the ancient Israelite equivalent of America's Law Day. For the Israelites, the Law, the Torah, was directly related to Israel's relationship with God. The Law wasn't just a set of rules; it was a description of how to live in covenant relationship with God. Celebrating God's gift of the Law meant celebrating the covenant that bound God and Israel together.

What combination of modern holidays might begin to match the significance of Pentecost (Feast of Weeks) to the Jews?

_____

Pentecost was a day of rest and worship, and it included specific sacrifices to be offered to the Lord as a gift of the first fruits (see Leviticus 23:15-17 and Numbers 28:26-31). After Solomon built the Temple in Jerusalem, Pentecost became one of the three pilgrimage feasts (along with Passover and Tabernacles), and all adult men of Israel were required to travel to Jerusalem to celebrate the rites of the feast in the sanctuary there.

This Old Testament background sets the stage for chapter 2 of Acts: "When the day of Pentecost had come..." (Acts 2:1). The Apostles gather together in Jerusalem, praying and waiting for Jesus to send the promise of the Father, and, on the day commemorating God's gift of the Law to his people at Mount Sinai, God sends his Holy Spirit on the faithful disciples, the new Israel. As St. Peter and the hundred and twenty disciples begin speaking in tongues, St. Luke tells us that "devout men from every nation under heaven" heard them speaking, each in his native language. Jerusalem was filled with this diverse crowd on this particular day because these faithful Jews had come to the Temple to celebrate Pentecost. And, upon hearing St. Peter's preaching, the hearts of the crowd are moved and thousands of them are baptized. When these new converts return home, they will become some of the first Christian missionaries, taking the good news of the Messiah to Mesopotamia, Egypt, Rome, and elsewhere, fulfilling the words of the prophet Isaiah: "And many peoples shall come, and say: 'Come, let us go up to the mountain of the LORD, to the house of the God of Jacob; that he may teach us his ways and that we may walk in his paths.' For out of Zion shall go forth the law, and the word of the LORD from Jerusalem" (Isaiah 2:3).

It is no coincidence that the Holy Spirit was given on the feast of Pentecost. There are many parallels between the Old Covenant feast of Pentecost and the New Covenant gift of the Spirit. For example, the feast of Pentecost was instituted as a harvest festival (Exodus 23:16), and St. Peter's preaching on Pentecost brought in the first fruits of the harvest of Christian converts.

Look up and compare the following Scripture passages and note some common elements between the old Pentecost and the new:

Old	New	Common Elements
Exodus 20:16-19, Exodus 24:17	Acts 2:2-4	
Exodus 32:25-28	Acts 2:41	

The Jewish feast of Pentecost celebrated the gift of the Law, and the Christian feast of Pentecost commemorates the gift of the Spirit. St. Paul's letters are full of comparisons between the Law of the Old Covenant and the grace we receive through the Holy Spirit in the New. St. Augustine summarizes this relationship by saying, "The law was given that grace might be sought; and grace was given, that the law might be fulfilled."

Look up Romans 7:12-16 and 8:2-4. Consider these passages and the quote from St. Augustine above. How does the gift of the Law at Mount Sinai prepare for the coming of the Holy Spirit at Pentecost?

_____

_____

_____

Allegory about the Old and the New Law / bpk, Berlin / Hamburger Kunsthalle / Art Resource, NY

St. Luke gives his account of Jesus' Ascension twice—once in his gospel and once in the Acts of the Apostles. As he returns to the Father, Jesus gives his Apostles his blessing and instructions for what to do next. Jesus' farewell to his closest friends can also prepare us to enter more fully into our mission to be his witnesses "to all nations" (Luke 24:47) and in all areas of our lives.

Vault. Pendentive with Ascension of Christ / Scala / Art Resource, NY

> **LECTIO:** The practice of praying with Scripture, *lectio divina*, begins with an active and close reading of the Scripture passage. Read the Scripture passage below and then answer the questions to take a closer look at some of the details of the passage.

"Then [Jesus] said to them, 'These are my words which I spoke to you, while I was still with you, that everything written about me in the law of Moses and the prophets and the psalms must be fulfilled.' Then he opened their minds to understand the Scriptures, and said to them, 'Thus it is written, that the Christ should suffer and on the third day rise from the dead, and that repentance and forgiveness of sins should be preached in his name to all nations, beginning from Jerusalem. You are witnesses of these things. And behold, I send the promise of my Father upon you; but stay in the city, until you are clothed with power from on high.' Then he led them out as far as Bethany, and lifting up his hands he blessed them. While he blessed them, he parted from them, and was carried up into heaven. And they returned to Jerusalem with great joy, and were continually in the temple blessing God." —Luke 24:44-53

What important words are repeated in this passage?

_____

What do the Apostles see during the Ascension?

_____

_____

What instructions does Jesus give his Apostles? What does he promise them?

_____

_____

> **MEDITATIO:** *Lectio*, a close reading and rereading, is followed by *meditatio*, time to reflect on the Scripture passage and to ponder the reason for particular events, descriptions, details, phrases, and even echoes from other Scripture passages that were noticed during *lectio*. Take some time now to meditate on the Scripture passage from page 35.

"In the Scripture readings the whole significance of Christ's Ascension is summarized for us. The richness of this mystery is spelled out in two statements: Jesus gave instructions, and then Jesus took his place. In the providence of God—in the eternal design of the Father —the hour had come for Christ to go away. He would leave his Apostles behind, with his Mother Mary, but only after he had given them his instructions. The Apostles now had a mission to perform according to the instructions that Jesus left, and these instructions were in turn the faithful expression of the Father's will. The instructions indicated, above all, that the Apostles were to wait for the Holy Spirit, who was the gift of the Father. From the beginning, it had to be crystal-clear that the source of the Apostles' strength is the Holy Spirit. It is the Holy Spirit who guides the Church in the way of truth; the Gospel is to spread through the power of God, and not by means of human wisdom or strength. The Apostles, moreover, were instructed to teach—to proclaim the Good News to the whole world. And they were to baptize in the name of the Father, and of the Son, and of the Holy Spirit. Like Jesus, they were to speak explicitly about the Kingdom of God and about salvation. The Apostles were to give witness to Christ to the ends of the earth. The early Church clearly understood these instructions and the missionary era began."

—Pope St. John Paul II, Homily on the Solemnity
of the Ascension of our Lord, May 24, 1979

What is the relationship between what was written (in the Law, the books of the prophets, and the psalms) about the Christ and the witness of the Apostles?

_____

_____

_____

Why does Pope St. John Paul II say it was important for the Apostles to wait for the Holy Spirit? Do you have the habit of "waiting on the Lord," of waiting for the direction of the Spirit? How can you develop this habit?

_____

_____

_____

Why do you think the Apostles were "continually in the temple blessing God" after Jesus ascended into Heaven? What implications does this have for your life and mission?

_____

_____

_____

ORATIO, CONTEMPLATIO, RESOLUTIO: Having read and meditated on today's Scripture passage, take some time to bring your thoughts to God (*oratio*) and engage God in silence (*contemplatio*). Then end your prayer by making a simple concrete resolution (*resolutio*) to respond to God's prompting of your heart in today's prayer.

_____

_____

_____

Vault. Pendentive with Ascension of Christ / Scala / Art Resource, NY

COMMIT—DAY 4
THE EFFECTS OF PENTECOST

"As the soul is the life of the body, so the Holy Spirit is the life of our souls."
—St. Peter Damian

It would be no exaggeration to say that Pentecost changed everything. The gift of the Holy Spirit transformed the Apostles, and through them the entire world. The effects of Pentecost can still be felt today, nearly 2,000 years after the initial event. In fact, every time a Catholic receives the Sacrament of Confirmation, he or she receives the exact same "promise of the Father" the early Christians received at Pentecost. And the anointing of the Spirit can have the same effects today as it did then.

Milan - little gold relief of Pentecost from Cappella Portinari
© Renata Sedmakova / shutterstock.com

Jesus promised the Apostles at the Last Supper that the Holy Spirit would teach them all things and remind them of everything he had said (see John 14:26). Before his Ascension, Jesus opened the minds of the Apostles to understand the Scriptures (see Luke 24:45). St. Peter, as the leader of the Apostles, is the first to demonstrate the effects of Pentecost. In his words and actions we see the Holy Spirit's gift of courage and understanding. His natural passion is refined in the Holy Spirit, and he preaches with boldness unthinkable in a man who fled at Jesus' arrest. Consider St. Peter's words to Jesus concerning his Passion in Matthew 16:22. How does his preaching at Pentecost demonstrate that the Holy Spirit has completely transformed his understanding?

_____

_____

While many in the crowd respond with faith to St. Peter's preaching, some are not so receptive—charging that the Apostles are merely drunk. But the reference to "new wine" in Acts 2:13 actually puts the gift of the Spirit at Pentecost into the important context of the fulfillment of messianic prophecy. Several Old Testament prophets used an abundance of wine as a metaphor for the outpouring of God's grace and favor in the messianic age. Isaiah 25 praises God for his wonderful deeds and foretells that in the day of the messiah the people will rejoice in God's salvation as God sets before all people a "feast of fat things, a feast of choice wines...of fat things full of marrow, of wine on the lees well refined" on Mount Zion (Isaiah 25:6). Joel 3:18 and Amos 9:13 both describe the mountains dripping with sweet wine when God restores the house of David by sending the messiah.

St. Peter explains to the crowd that the Apostles are not drunk on wine (not only is it around nine in the morning, it is both too early and inappropriate to be drinking), but they are filled with the new wine of the Spirit. Just as new wine cannot be put into old wineskins without causing them to burst (Matthew 9:17), the new wine of the Spirit cannot be put into the old wineskin of a heart that is hardened by sin, and so Peter calls on his listeners to "Repent, and be baptized every one of you in the name of Jesus Christ for the forgiveness of your sins; and you shall receive the gift of the Holy Spirit" (Acts 2:38).

St. Paul beautifully describes the effect and the fruits of being filled with the new wine of the Holy Spirit. Look up Romans 5:5 and Galatians 5:22-23. What effect and fruits does Paul describe? Have you witnessed these fruits in your own life or the lives of other Christians? In the Sacraments of Baptism and Confirmation we receive the same Spirit the Apostles received at Pentecost. How is God calling you to rediscover these effects and fruits of the Spirit in your own life?

Traditional wineskin made of leather © Alfonso de Tomas / shutterstock.com

_____

_____

O Holy Spirit,
Divine Spirit of light and love,
I consecrate to Thee my understanding, heart, and will,
my whole being for time and eternity.
May my understanding be always submissive
to Thy heavenly inspirations
and to the teaching of the Catholic Church,
of which Thou art the Infallible Guide.
May my heart be ever inflamed
with love of God and of my neighbor.
May my will be ever conformed to the Divine will;
and may my whole life be a faithful imitation of the life
and virtues of our Lord and Savior Jesus Christ,
to whom with the Father and Thee,
be honor and glory forever.
Amen.

COMMIT—DAY 5
TRUTH AND BEAUTY

Pentecost, Jean Bourdichon, c. 1503-1508,
from the Grand Hours of Anne of Brittany in the Bibliothéque Nationale de France, Paris.

Pentecost / © BnF, Dist. RMN-Grand Palais / Art Resource, NY

Jean Bourdichon was a late fifteenth to early sixteenth-century miniature painter who illustrated numerous manuscripts, including the "Grand Hours of Anne of Brittany," which contains this Pentecost painting. A book of hours was a devotional prayer book, popular in the Middle Ages, containing a collection of texts, prayers, and psalms. Typically these were a version of the Divine Office (Liturgy of the Hours) prayed in monasteries, but abbreviated for lay people who desired to incorporate monastic prayer into their devotional life.

While most such books contained minimal illustrations—decorated capital letters to begin a prayer or psalm—the prayer books of wealthy patrons could include numerous miniature paintings taking up a portion or full page. For the French Queen, Anne of Brittany, her Grand Hours contained not only beautifully detailed margin illustrations of plants and insects, but also nearly fifty full-page illustrations. These miniature paintings, interspersed amongst the readings and prayers, provided a visual storytelling to enhance the reader's prayer and meditation.

Look up Acts 1:14-15 and 2:1. Who is present when the Spirit descends on Pentecost?

_____

_____

In Bourdichon's *Pentecost*, Mary sits at the center, hands folded in prayer, recalling St. Luke's description that all "with one accord devoted themselves to prayer, together with…Mary the mother of Jesus" (Acts 1:14). She is encircled by the Twelve Apostles, and behind them numerous disciples fill the room. Halos surround the heads not only of Mary and the Apostles, but also the other disciples, all of whom make up the "brethren" (Acts 1:15). As in many of Bourdichon's paintings in the Grand Hours, the two Apostles in the foreground are shown only down to their knees, bringing them closer to the viewer so as to draw her into the story or event presented and aid in meditation. Here, these two Apostles in the foreground are so close that the viewer can imagine herself as one of the disciples surrounding the Apostles on this side of the room.

Mary and the saints are robed with rich colors. Her purple tunic is covered with a pure white veil/collar and a rich blue cloak. In Christian art, blue symbolizes the sky, the heavens, and even divinity. Mary has been depicted in blue since the fifth century, as it was the color of a Byzantine empress—also fitting due to Mary's role as the Queen of Heaven. The Apostles around her wear shades of yellow, red, green, blue, and purple, and in those closest golden highlights mark the folds of their garments.

Pentecost / © BnF, Dist. RMN-Grand Palais / Art Resource, NY

Mary's gaze is directed at the viewer, inviting us into the scene, where the gaze of the Apostles draws our attention upward to the Holy Spirit, in the form of a pure white dove, who enters the room through the oculus (the circular opening at the dome's apex). Instead of tongues of fire, Bourdichon portrays the promised gift of the Father emanating from the dove as golden rays (this is the same representation he will use in portraying the Holy Spirit overshadowing Mary in his Annunciation painting in this same book). The Latin inscription in the lower picture frame recalls Acts 2:4: "They were all filled with the Holy Spirit and began to speak with a great number of tongues." Bourdichon's painting captures the moment of the Holy Spirit's outpouring, and we can imagine that at any instant we might hear the pictured disciples singing God's praises in a multitude of languages.

Bourdichon has placed the event of Pentecost in a circular room—its shape highlighted by the circle of Apostles around Mary—which with its repeated niches and open dome calls to mind the Pantheon, a Roman temple dedicated to "all the gods." Its dome was, and is, an architectural marvel at 142 feet in diameter; it wasn't until the fifteenth century, just a couple decades before Bourdichon's birth, that a dome of equal size was again built. While the room's architectural style hints at the glory of Rome, its bleak gray color stands in stark contrast to the vibrant colors which dress the saints being filled with God's own Spirit, perhaps highlighting the reality that the temporal glories of the pagan world pale in comparison to the new life found in Jesus Christ and the gift of God's Spirit.

In the early seventh century, the Pantheon was converted to a Christian church and consecrated to St. Mary and the Martyrs. If Bourdichon intends a Pantheon-like room for his Pentecost painting, then his placement of Mary surrounded by the Apostles, eleven of whom die a martyr's death, highlights the Christian name of this church. The placement of the dove of the Holy Spirit descending through the oculus on Mary and the Apostles and disciples recalls an ancient custom that has been revived in our own day where, on the feast of Pentecost, rose petals are dropped from the Church of St. Mary and the Martyrs' (the Pantheon's) oculus down upon those worshipping, reminding them of the tongues of fire that rested on those present in Jerusalem at the first Pentecost.

With the gift of the Holy Spirit at the first Pentecost, the disciples went out evangelizing from Jerusalem, to Samaria, to Asia minor, and eventually to Rome, whose empire stretched to the "end of the earth," fulfilling Jesus' words at his Ascension (Acts 1:8). This evangelization eventually won over the hearts of pagan Rome, turning it into a Christian civilization. As our own day and age turns more and more away from the gospel, the same Holy Spirit that Mary and the Apostles and disciples received at Pentecost desires to empower each of us to go out anew with the same gospel mercy and grace to our families, our friends, and once again even to the ends of the earth.

Take a moment to journal your ideas, questions, or insights about this lesson. Write down thoughts you had that may not have been mentioned in the text or the discussion questions. List any personal applications you got from the lessons. What challenged you the most in the teachings? How might you turn what you've learned into specific action?

_____

_____

_____

_____

_____

_____

_____

SESSION 3

PROCLAIMING THE KERYGMA

OPENING PRAYER

Come Holy Spirit,
fill the hearts of your faithful
and enkindle in them the fire of your love.
Send forth your Spirit
and they shall be created.
And you shall renew the face of the earth.

Let us pray. O, God,
who did instruct the hearts of the faithful
by the light of the Holy Spirit,
grant that by the same Holy Spirit
we may be truly wise
and ever rejoice in his consolation.
Through Christ our Lord, Amen.

St. Peter, pray for us.

INTRODUCTION

The outpouring of the Holy Spirit at Pentecost is a
moment of power and grace for the early Church.
Whereas the Apostles cowered in fear after the
death of Jesus, now they joyfully and publically
proclaim the events that they have witnessed.
Before the Holy Spirit came upon him powerfully
at Pentecost, St. Peter denied Jesus three
times; now he boldly proclaims Jesus Christ
crucified, died, and risen to many thousands of
people in the capital city of Jerusalem. The
difference is the Holy Spirit. Let's take a closer look
at the message that the Holy Spirit inspired
Peter to preach on that first Pentecost.

Pentecost / Scala / Art Resource, NY

43

CONNECT

This week we will explore how the Holy Spirit worked in the early Church. The conversion stories are fascinating: St. Anthony of the Desert had a conversion of heart when hearing the words of Jesus in Matthew 19:21; St. Augustine's conversion occurred while reading Romans 13:13-14; St. Teresa Benedicta of the Cross (Edith Stein) experienced conversion after staying up all night reading St. Teresa of Avila's *Life*. What is your own conversion story?

Can you share a recent homily that really moved or struck you? What was it about the preaching or topic that made it so memorable? How has it affected you?

DISCUSS

PART 1: PETER'S PENTECOST SERMON
Watch the teaching on video. The following is a brief outline of the topics covered.

I. First Papal Address – This Is It! (Acts: 2: 14-36)

II. Joel
    A. Jesus is anointed/baptized with the Holy Spirit
    B. Outpouring of the Spirit on everybody
    C. Recalls 70 elders—Numbers 11:25-29

III. Psalm 16
    A. David died and his tomb is here, but
        Jesus' tomb is empty
    B. We are all witnesses of the Resurrection
        of the Christ
    C. Acts 2:33—"This which you see and hear";
        gift of Holy Spirit is perceptible

IV. Response of the Crowd
   A. "Cut to the heart...what shall we do?"
   B. "Repent, and be baptized"

DISCUSS

1. What is the initial reaction of the people of Jerusalem to this great outpouring of the Holy Spirit at Pentecost?

_____

_____

2. How does St. Peter explain what is occurring to the crowd? How does he use the Scriptures to show that what the people of Israel have longed for has now taken place?

_____

_____

3. When the crowd asks, "What shall we do?" how does St. Peter respond?

_____

_____

PART 2: WHAT IS THE KERYGMA?
Watch the video teaching. The following is a brief outline of the topics covered.

I. St. Peter Proclaimed the Kerygma (Acts 4:12)
   A. Kerygma—Greek for message or
      announcement
   B. Core message of the good news
   C. Differentiate between kerygma and catechesis
      1. Kerygma (proclamation to those who
         haven't heard the gospel)
      2. Catechesis (instruction in doctrine and morals)

II. Characteristics of the Kerygma Message
   A. Intrinsic power of announcing "Jesus is Lord"
   B. Kerygma is Christocentric (Christ-centered)
      1. Is our evangelizing Christocentric? Or is it
         ecclesiocentric (church-centered)
         or something else?
      2. Cardinal Avery Dulles: "The Church,
         therefore, has one inescapable task:
         to lift up Christ"
   C. Message of Salvation (Acts 4:12)
      and Countercultural (1 Corinthians 1:21-25)

DISCUSS

4. What is the core message of the Gospel, that which is included in the kerygma?

_____

5. What does it mean when we say that there is an intrinsic power to the kerygma?

_____

6. What does it mean that the kerygma is a message of salvation? How does this relate to the critical importance of missionary activity and evangelization?

_____

_____

_____

PART 3: EVANGELIZATION
Watch the video teaching. The following is a brief outline of the topics covered.

I. Evangelization
   A. *Evangelion*—Greek meaning "good news"
   B. Christians proclaim greatest good news
   C. Evangelization is to do what Jesus did

II. Two Senses of Evangelization
   (*Evangelii Nuntiandi*)
   A. Strict sense—proclaiming the kerygma
   B. Broad sense—everything in Church's mission
      1. Proclaiming the kerygma
      2. Catechesis and sacraments
      3. Ongoing faith formation
      4. Pastoral care
      5. Transformation of society

III. Four Characteristics of the Life of the Church
      1. Apostles' teaching (Creed)
      2. Breaking of bread (Sacraments)
      3. Fellowship (Moral life)
      4. Prayers (Prayer)

IV. How Does this Apply to Us Today?
   A. Many need to hear the kerygma today
      1. Pope Bl. Paul VI: "The split between the gospel and culture is without a doubt the drama of our time"
      2. Pope St. John Paul II: "Many Catholics have been baptized and catechized, without ever having been evangelized."
      (*Catechesi Tradendae*, 19)

DISCUSS

7. Conversion is not a one-time event; normally, God uses many people, events, and experiences to bring us to him. In evangelization, we do need to use words to proclaim the kerygma, to boldly share the Gospel. However, Dr. Healy explains that all the Church's activity can be considered evangelization. What is included in evangelization in this broad sense? How is this different from evangelization in the strict sense?

_____

_____

8. What are the four characteristics of the life of the early Church? What can we do today to incorporate these essential aspects into our daily/weekly lives? What does it mean to create a Christian culture? What would that look like with regard to entertainment, our leisure time, family life, our behavior at work, etc.?

_____

_____

MEMORY VERSE

"And they devoted themselves to the apostles' teaching and fellowship, to the breaking of bread and the prayers."
—Acts 2:42

CLOSING PRAYER

Lord Jesus, you poured out your Spirit upon the Apostles at Pentecost,
inaugurating the new age of the Church.
You inspired St. Peter with a zeal to proclaim your truth to the crowd that gathered.
Through his words and the power of the Holy Spirit, 3,000 were converted that day.
Lord Jesus Christ, crucified, died, and risen from the dead:
give us the special grace of the Holy Spirit to boldly proclaim the Gospel.
Give us zeal for souls, so that we long for people to come to know you
in a deep and personal way. We ask that you banish our fears and anxieties
so that we can step out in faith and courage as St. Peter did
in front of those many thousands of his countrymen.
We ask this in your holy name. Amen.

St. Peter, pray for us.

FOR FURTHER READING

Pope Francis, *Evangelii Gaudium (The Joy of the Gospel)*

Pope Blessed Paul VI, *Evangelii Nutiandi (Evangelization in the Modern World)*

Pope St. John Paul II, *Redemptoris Missio (Mission of the Redeemer)*

Golden rays of the sun breaking through the storm clouds © kosmos111 / shutterstock.com

People have been experiencing "aha" moments long before Archimedes exclaimed "Eureka!" This type of moment is characterized by a brilliant flash of insight into a long-deliberated problem—and it's often of such vital importance that it may change the course of the person's life. For Samuel Morse, a personal tragedy was the impetus for this "aha" moment. Trained as a painter, he was in Washington, D.C., painting a portrait of the famous Marquis de Lafayette, when he received a letter from his father in Connecticut explaining that his wife was gravely ill. He immediately left. By the time he reached his home, his wife was dead and already buried. This became his inspiration for dedicating his life to improve methods of communication, resulting in the invention of the telegraph.

Have you ever experienced a sudden insight into a long-contemplated problem that changed the course of your life? Explain.

_____

_____

St. Peter preaching / Alfredo Dagli Orti / The Art Archive at Art Resource, NY

In the first century, the problem for the Jews was much more perplexing than the need to communicate quickly over great distances. The future of the nation of Israel (and their personal futures) was at stake. The prophets had foretold that the messiah's coming was imminent and that salvation was at hand. As Dr. Healy explained, St. Peter is telling the people gathered around him in Jerusalem, "This is it!" Everything that the patriarchs longed for, all the prophets prophesied about, and what the psalms sang about...all that the Jews were eagerly awaiting has now come in Jesus Christ. From this point on, everything is different.

When a crowd gathers, perplexed at what is happening to the disciples at Pentecost, St. Peter is inspired by the Holy Spirit and explains this event in a way that would "prove," or compellingly make a case for, what is occurring. In order to make this point, to show how Jesus in his life, Death, and Resurrection was the fulfillment of the Old

Covenant, St. Peter draws upon two passages from the Old Testament: Joel 2 and Psalm 16. If we do not know the Old Testament Scriptures as well as this first-century audience, we might miss the point of the beginning of this first papal address. But these devout Jews and God-fearers knew the Scriptures and expected a messiah who would fulfill the Law and the Prophets, so St. Peter's references to such Old Testament passages would have made perfect sense.

St. Peter quotes Joel 2:28-32. The prophet Joel regales his listeners with a great eschatological vision in which the Spirit is poured out, not just on prophets, but on all men and women. Dr. Healy explained how the prophet Joel had in mind what Moses said to Joshua, "Would that all the LORD's people were prophets" (Numbers 11:29). It is significant here that Joel's great vision of this giving of the Spirit is ubiquitous; it includes not only men, but women as well! This marvelous and inspiring vision is followed by something that does not sound so wonderful: "And I will give portents in the heavens and on the earth, blood and fire and columns of smoke. The sun shall be turned to darkness, and the moon to blood, before the great and terrible day of the LORD comes" (Joel 2:30-31). What? We were enjoying a wonderful vision of God coming to his people and pouring out his Spirit, and now it seems like we are in the midst of an apocalyptic movie. What is Joel talking about?

The prophet Joel / Erich Lessing / Art Resource, NY

Eschatological: Refers to the last days or the fulfillment of God's promise to deliver and restore Israel.

Apocalyptic language: Symbolic language used to describe the events surrounding the coming of the LORD to deliver and restore Israel, usually in the context of vision and prophecy.

The context for Joel's prophecy is essential. Before the exile of God's people from the Promised Land, Joel prophesies the Day of the Lord and calls God's people to repentance. In this passage, Joel speaks about the Day of the Lord, which will be attested to with signs and wonders and the outpouring of the Spirit. The prophet then goes on to prophesy about the destruction of Judah, which eventually occurs because God's people do not repent. The prophets use apocalyptic language to describe the end of a political system. They oftentimes represent it in terms of the end of the world, because that is what it is like for the people experiencing it.

When St. Peter quotes Joel, he deliberately references both parts of the prophecy. He uses the first part to show that God's promise centuries ago to pour out his Spirit is now being fulfilled because of Jesus' Death, Resurrection, and Ascension. With Jesus' return to the Father in Heaven, God pours out his Spirit just as Jesus promised at the Last Supper: "For if I do not go away, the Counselor will not come to you; but if I go, I will send him to you" (John 16:7).

St. Peter quotes the second part of Joel's prophecy as both a spiritual warning of the consequences of sin and also as a temporal warning to those gathered that a disaster is coming upon Jerusalem. His use of Joel's apocalyptic language is actually very appropriate, for within one generation, in 70 AD, the Roman army would destroy Jerusalem and the Temple, as Peter hints at here, and in fact as Jesus himself explicitly prophesied in Matthew 24:1-2. Indeed Josephus, a first-century Jewish historian and eyewitness to the terrible destruction of Jerusalem, describes it in language just as cataclysmic as the prophet Joel.

> *"A supernatural apparition was seen, too amazing to be believed. What I am now to relate would, I imagine, be dismissed as imaginary, had this not been vouched for by eyewitnesses, then followed by subsequent disasters that deserved to be thus signalized. For before sunset chariots were seen in the air over the whole country, and armed battalions speeding through the clouds and encircling the cities."*
> —Josephus, *War of the Jews*, Book VI, Chapter V, paragraph 3 rendered in Chilton

The Holy Trinity / Scala / Art Resource, NY

Josephus describes the spiritual realities of the battle and the subsequent destruction of Jerusalem accomplished by Rome's army.

What is the answer to this day of distress? The answer, according to St. Peter and Joel: Call upon the name of the Lord. Peter closes his preaching exhorting the people, "Save yourselves," and with specific instructions, "Repent, and be baptized every one of you *in the name of Jesus Christ* for the forgiveness of your sins; and you shall receive the gift of the Holy Spirit" (Acts 2:38, emphasis added). God is coming to his people with charismatic signs and prophecy as well as judgment and a new age. This would be a great "eureka" moment for those gathered. That which many prophets had described is now coming to pass.

Now for the heart of the matter. It is an exciting moment! Many Jews anticipated that when the Messiah came, he would inaugurate this great end of the age described by Joel and the other prophets. Having shown that this new age has come with God's outpouring of his Spirit, St. Peter has set the stage to introduce the person of Jesus Christ. So it shouldn't surprise us that his next words are "Men of Israel, hear these words: Jesus of Nazareth ..." (Acts 2:22).

Look at Luke 24:44-48 and Acts 1:8; 1:22; 2:32. What are St. Peter and the Apostles called to be?

_____

Look up John 21:24 and Acts 2:36; 2:40; 3:1-15. What are some ways that the Apostles give this witness?

_____

St. Peter, as is clear from the first chapter of Acts, clearly recognizes his and the other Apostles' role as messengers of Jesus, sent to the world to be witnesses to the Resurrection. When he stands up to preach on Pentecost, this is exactly what he does.

St. Peter uses Psalm 16 and Psalm 110 to prove two important points about Jesus. What are they? Explain the argument that he makes using these psalms in your own words.

Saint Peter Preaching in the Presence of Saint Mark / Scala/Ministero per i Beni e le Attività culturali / Art Resource, NY

_____

_____

_____

Because of his Jewish audience, St. Peter's appeal to the authority of David's words is a critical component of his argument. Yet it is not the most essential part. What if he were not speaking to men of Judea and Jerusalem? Even without David's prophetic words from the Psalms, what is the key point St. Peter makes?

_____

_____

Later on St. Peter will write, "Always be prepared to make a defense to any one who calls you to account for the hope that is in you" (1 Peter 3:15). Acts of the Apostles shows Peter and the first Christian disciples doing this over and over again. Peter knew his audience on Pentecost and made use of the Old Testament Prophets and Psalms. Later when he encounters a lame man, he simply instructs him, in Jesus' name, to "walk," proclaiming Jesus' Death and Resurrection as the source of the miracle. Peter responds to the needs of each audience, but the core message of the gospel remains the same. We too are called to "always be ready" to proclaim the central gospel message, the kerygma, and the work of God in our own lives.

In *Evangelii Gaudium,* Pope Francis offers the following advice on what the kerygma should contain: "The centrality of the kerygma calls for stressing those elements which are most needed today: it has to express God's saving love." In his exhortation, he provides us with an example of the kerygma: "Jesus Christ loves you; he gave his life to save you; and now he is living at your side every day to enlighten, strengthen and free you," and he emphasizes that the kerygma should be at the "centre of all evangelizing activity and all efforts at Church renewal." This is essential for us as missionary disciples. We must have the kerygma ready to proclaim when the opportunity arises—just as St. Peter proclaimed the core message of salvation on Pentecost and thousands were baptized due to its proclamation.

The Apostles were different after Pentecost. They had willingly followed Jesus for three years and endured hardship for his sake, but they were not able to proclaim the saving truth of Jesus Christ prior to Pentecost. As Pope St. John Paul II states: "The Spirit transformed them." We do not proclaim the kerygma on our own; the Spirit transforms us and allows us to speak these words with power.

God the Father and the Holy Spirit / National Trust Photo Library / Art Resource, NY

"Despite their love for him and their generous response to his call, they proved to be incapable of understanding his words and reluctant to follow him along the path of suffering and humiliation. The Spirit transformed them into courageous witnesses to Christ and enlightened heralds of his word. It was the Spirit himself who guided them along the difficult and new paths of mission."
                                                        —Pope St. John Paul II, *Redemptoris Missio,* 87

St. Peter's preaching consists not merely of words and arguments, but of the power of the Holy Spirit. By the Spirit, the preaching is effective and bears fruit: 3,000 come to faith and are baptized. As Dr. Healy mentioned, the truth, in a sense, speaks for itself. Let's take a closer look at the response of the crowd to the truth that Peter preached that first Pentecost morning.

Saint John Baptizing Christ in the river Jordan / Alfredo Dagli Orti / The Art Archive at Art Resource, NY

LECTIO: The practice of praying with Scripture, *lectio divina*, begins with an active and close reading of the Scripture passage. Read the verse below and then answer the questions to take a closer look at some of the details of the passage.

> *"'Let all the house of Israel therefore know assuredly that God has made him both Lord and Christ, this Jesus whom you crucified.' Now when they heard this they were cut to the heart and said to Peter and the rest of the apostles, 'Brethren, what shall we do?' And Peter said to them, 'Repent, and be baptized every one of you in the name of Jesus Christ for the forgiveness of your sins; and you shall receive the gift of the Holy Spirit. For the promise is to you and to your children and to all that are far off, everyone whom the Lord our God calls to him.' And he testified with many other words and exhorted them, saying, 'Save yourselves from this crooked generation.' So those who received his word were baptized, and there were added that day about three thousand souls. And they devoted themselves to the apostles' teaching and fellowship, to the breaking of bread and the prayers."* —Acts 2:36–42

To whom does St. Peter address his words in Acts 2:36, as opposed to the beginning of his preaching (Acts 2:14)?

_____

St. Luke tells us that the people present were "cut to the heart." What words of St. Peter elicited this reaction? Compare this to the initial response to the disciples' behavior in Acts 2:12–13.

_____

_____

What does St. Peter tell them to do? What does he say will be the result?

_____

_____

What marks the life of those baptized (Acts 2:42)?

_____

_____

_____

MEDITATIO: *Lectio*, a close reading and rereading, is followed by *meditatio*, time to reflect on the Scripture passage and to ponder the reason for particular events, descriptions, details, phrases, and even echoes from other Scripture passages that were noticed during *lectio*. Take some time now to meditate on the Scripture verses of today's *lectio*.

Let's take a few moments and reflect on where St. Peter has been for the past fifty days. First of all, he is with Jesus at the Last Supper and the Garden of Gethsemane, where he abandons Jesus along with the other Apostles. When he comes to his senses, he follows Jesus to the house of the high priest, where he denies Jesus three times. After the Crucifixion, he is hiding with the Apostles when the women bring them the news of the Resurrection. He rushes out to the tomb to find only linen cloths and no Jesus. Later, Jesus appears to him and the other Apostles, and he witnesses the Ascension of Jesus. Jesus tells the disciples and Peter to wait in Jerusalem until they receive the Holy Spirit. The book of Acts opens with the disciples following Jesus' instructions, waiting in Jerusalem. They are together praying when the Holy Spirit is poured out upon them, and they experience those extraordinary phenomena recorded in Acts. We nowhere see St. Peter acting as he did after Pentecost. Whereas before he ran away and denied Jesus, now he is boldly proclaiming Jesus as the Messiah that they have been longing for! Pentecost changes Peter. As Pope St. John Paul II, speaking of the Apostles, stated, "The Spirit transformed them into courageous witnesses to Christ and enlightened heralds of his word" (*Redemptoris Missio*, 87). Now Peter boldly announces the gospel and challenges his hearers to accept Jesus, repent, and be baptized. Repent in Greek is related to *metanoia*, which means conversion. This is not merely sorrow or regret for sins, but a turning away from sin and changing one's life—conversion. We cannot do this on our own but only through the power of the Holy Spirit. What happens at Peter's preaching is what happens when people encounter Christ in the gospels, and also today when people come into contact with Christ: conversion, a total change, a reorientation of one's life. Peter's words and the grace of the Holy Spirit move the people to sincerely ask, "What should we do?" Christ's forgiveness and the gift of the Holy Spirit require an action on our part; we need to repent and receive Baptism, which confers the grace of the Holy Spirit.

Put yourself in St. Peter's place. Several weeks ago you had denied Jesus. Since then you have seen Jesus resurrected, received his forgiveness, and seen him ascend into Heaven—and now, tongues of fire and the outpouring of the Spirit at Pentecost. Only weeks ago you hid for fear that you too might be arrested, and now the Holy Spirit prompts you to start speaking to the crowd. What does it take to say that first word? How might Peter's experience help you when you feel the Holy Spirit directing you to step out in faith?

The Conversion of Saint Paul / Restored Tradition Art

_____

_____

The crowd is "cut to the heart." Jesus Christ is the answer to every human heart. He is what each person desires and longs for. In the person of Christ, we see who we are meant to be. As the Second Vatican Council states, "[Jesus Christ] fully reveals man to man himself and makes his supreme calling clear" (*Gaudium et Spes*, 22). How does Jesus reveal you to yourself? What is the supreme calling God calls each of us to?

_____

_____

St. Peter informs the crowd that they must repent and be baptized in order to receive the Holy Spirit. Have you experienced this forgiveness of sins in Baptism and in the Sacrament of Reconciliation? At our Baptism we are cleansed of all sin and receive the Holy Spirit and his sanctifying grace. This grace is strengthened at Confirmation. How does this grace of the Holy Spirit living in your soul affect your life? How can you recall this special gift that you have received each day? How can the Holy Spirit and grace in your soul be increased and strengthened? Living in Christ and his Spirit should mean a new way of life, a Christian culture in every aspect of our lives. How can we each live out the four marks of a Christian (Acts 2:42) in our lives?

_____

_____

ORATIO, CONTEMPLATIO, RESOLUTIO: Having read and meditated on today's Scripture passage, take some time to bring your thoughts to God (*oratio*) and engage God in silence (*contemplatio*). Then end your prayer by making a simple concrete resolution (*resolutio*) to respond to God's prompting of your heart in today's prayer.

COMMIT–DAY 4
THE CALL TO EVANGELIZATION

Since the Great Commission, from apostolic times to the present day, many men and women have answered the call to bring the gospel to those who do not know Jesus Christ. Recently canonized St. Junipero Serra stands among those great saints who left behind what the world had to offer in order to bring the gospel "to the ends of the earth." In the mid-eighteenth century, he had a promising career teaching philosophy in the university on an island off the coast of Spain, but he was not content. He had an ambition to be a missionary to the New World. With one other companion, he left his native Mallorca, set ablaze with zeal to evangelize the Americas.

> *"What made Friar Junípero leave his home and country, his family, university chair and Franciscan community in Mallorca to go to the ends of the earth? Certainly, it was the desire to proclaim the Gospel* ad gentes *[to the nations], that heartfelt impulse which seeks to share with those farthest away the gift of encountering Christ: a gift that he had first received and experienced in all its truth and beauty. Like Paul and Barnabas, like the disciples in Antioch and in all of Judea, he was filled with joy and the Holy Spirit in spreading the word of the Lord. Such zeal excites us, it challenges us!"*
> —Pope Francis, Homily on the Canonization of St. Junipero Serra

Junipero Serra, Spanish missionary who founded missionaries in California
© Everett Historical / shutterstock.com

Serra, known for his personal holiness and zealous action, evangelized the Native Americans in what is now California, establishing nine missions along its coast. He taught agriculture and animal husbandry and also encouraged expressions of culture. He defended the rights of the natives against corrupt Spanish settlers. In a nutshell, he evangelized the area and established a Christian culture.

Is reflecting on the foreign missions exciting to you? Have you met a foreign missionary before? Have you been on a mission trip? How can you support the Church's mission to bring the truth of Jesus Christ to those who have never heard the gospel?

_____

_____

While inspiring, such stories of missionary zeal can also seem far removed from our experience. But they shouldn't! Even though over 200 years separate us from St. Junipero Serra, the charge to each Christian remains the same. Pope Francis exhorts us that the same reason for Junipero Serra's missionary zeal—"These missionary disciples who have encountered Jesus, the Son of God, who have come to know him through his merciful Father, moved by the grace of the Holy Spirit, went out to all the geographical, social and existential peripheries, to bear witness to charity"—also should compel each of us to evangelize: "Every Christian is a missionary to the extent that he or she has encountered the love of God in Christ Jesus" (*Evangelii Gaudium*, 120). Each one of us is a missionary—not just those sent to foreign countries, but every Christian. We are each called to evangelize.

Can you recall a time when you felt moved to share your faith with someone else? Or that you answered someone's question about Christianity? At that moment, you shared in the Church's call to bring Jesus to the world. That is what is meant by evangelization. Evangelization is not just a one-time event. Many formerly Christian nations are now places of little faith. We need to continually proclaim the saving truth of Jesus Christ to each generation, just as those early missionaries did so zealously. This is what is meant by the New Evangelization.

> "I sense that the moment has come to commit all of the Church's energies to a new evangelization and to the mission ad gentes [to the nations]. No believer in Christ, no institution of the Church can avoid this supreme duty: to proclaim Christ to all peoples."
> —Pope St. John Paul II, *Redemptoris Missio*, 3

To bring the gospel to others we must evangelize using every means available to us. Not only this, but we must attempt to bring Jesus to every level of society and human activity. Pope Pius X, who died over 100 years ago, saw the miserable state of the world around him and resolved to spend his pontificate emphasizing the need to "restore all things in Christ," a phrase he borrowed from St. Paul. He underscored personal holiness as the goal of each Christian and then the importance of bringing Christ to each aspect of one's life: family, work, and society.

Too often we tend to absorb the prevailing culture around us. Sometimes our lives look almost identical to our non-Catholic, non-Christian, neighbors: we watch the same movies, spend hours surfing the web, and obsess over newly acquired gadgets. What would it look like if we allowed the truth of Jesus and the gospel to transform each aspect of our lives? Give some examples of how that would affect what you do with your free time, your time at work, leisure at home with your family, etc.

_____

_____

The old-fashioned term "zeal for souls" is an important starting point of evangelization. Zeal for souls describes that love of neighbor that causes us to long for their conversion, which ultimately leads to eternal life. Zeal for souls motivates us to do whatever we can to be a channel of God's love and grace to that neighbor. St. Teresa of Avila described her zeal for souls this way: "It breaks my heart to see so many souls traveling to perdition....I felt that I would have laid down a thousand lives to save a single one of all the souls that were being lost" (*The Way of Perfection*, 1). Longing for souls is essential for a Christian; it is an imitation of Jesus who poured out his blood for the salvation of souls.

Is God calling you to increase your zeal for a particular family member, friend, or neighbor? Commit to praying for this person. What first step can you make to begin a new or deeper relationship with this person?

_____

_____

An icon with the picture of the Merciful Jesus © GoneWithTheWind / shutterstock.com

57

COMMIT—DAY 5
TRUTH AND BEAUTY

St. Peter Preaching to the Multitude, Masolino da Panicale, c. 1424-25,
Brancacci Chapel, Church of Santa Maria del Carmine, Florence, Italy

Saint Peter preaching to the people / Alfredo Dagli Orti / The Art Archive at Art Resource, NY

At the end of the fourteenth century, Pietro Brancacci commissioned the construction of
a chapel in the right transept of the Church of Santa Maria del Carmine in Florence, Italy.
Once constructed, his descendant, Felice Brancacci, commissioned Masolino da Panicale
and his young associate, Masaccio, to paint a series of frescoes with scenes from the life
of St. Peter, Pietro's patron saint. The resulting fresco cycle is one of the masterpieces of
Renaissance painting, and earned the chapel the oft-used title of the "Sistine chapel of the
early Renaissance."

The frescoes in this chapel put on display the best painting of their day, using linear perspective to give volume and depth to the scenes, and *chiaroscuro* (the use of light and shadow) to bring the scenes to life. The buildings and/or mountains, which are the backdrop of the various events portrayed, continue in adjacent works, providing a spatial unity to the scenes as they progress around the chapel walls.

The chapel's frescoes include Adam and Eve's sin and subsequent expulsion from the Garden of Eden, as well as Jesus' response to the question of payment of the tribute tax, but the remaining scenes are primarily drawn from the Acts of the Apostles and recount St. Peter's lead role in the early Church and her evangelization through preaching, miracles, and suffering. In each of the scenes we can identify Peter with his curly white hair and beard. A simple fisherman, his feet are not shod with sandals. Masolino clothes Peter in a blue tunic, wrapped in a rich gold robe. The vibrant colors of the various robes, in this scene and even more so in other scenes in the Brancacci chapel, highlight the masterful wool and silk production that was a prominent part of Florence's economy.

Masolino's *St. Peter Preaching to the Multitude* recalls St. Peter's first post-Pentecost preaching. Acts recounts how Peter, filled with the Holy Spirit and "standing with the eleven, lifted up his voice" and addressed the gathering multitude, which was bewildered at hearing the disciples speaking in a myriad of different tongues (Acts 2). While we do not see the other eleven Apostles in the Masolino's fresco, we do behold a varied crowd of men and women, young and old.

Look up Acts 2:12-13. How is the response of the crowd described?

_____

Look up Acts 2:36-37. What will be the response of the crowd to St. Peter's preaching?

_____

_____

Acts recounts the various responses from the crowd—mocking, amazement, perplexity, and conviction. These and more we see portrayed in the faces in the crowd, from the placid attention of the veiled nun in the foreground, to the anxiety of the woman whose fearful eyes are all we see. An old man in front is so sound asleep that he no longer looks at St. Peter. Will Peter's preaching awaken his mind and heart? In contrast, the woman next to him listens carefully to his words, attentive to all that he recounts. A younger woman rests her head on her hand, eyes closed, but with a countenance of unexpected serenity and peace, given Peter's serious indictment. Perhaps her countenance foreshadows that she will be one of the 3,000 who receive his word that day and are baptized—receiving in those waters the peace that only Christ can give.

St. Peter looks at the crowd with an intensity that underscores the importance of the testimony he gives. Just as he will "direct his gaze" at the lame man and bring him healing in Jesus' name (Acts 3), so now he looks out at the multitude exhorting them to "Repent, and be baptized... in the name of Jesus Christ" (Acts 2:38). While the event takes place in the first century, Masolino has included in the gathered assembly contemporaries of his day, dressed in the capes and caps common in fifteenth-century Florence. He also includes friars, with their tonsured haircuts, and religious sisters in their habits, a common sight in Santa Maria del Carmine and throughout Florence.

Placing contemporaries of the day in St. Peter's audience extended an invitation to all who entered the Brancacci chapel, in the fifteenth century and today, to see themselves as one of those to whom Peter addresses his exhortation. Like Peter's first-century audience, we are called to hear this Apostle's words directed to us anew: "This Jesus whom you crucified…." We are invited to ponder our own attentiveness and response to Peter's words. Are we asleep? Are we listening? Are we "cut to the heart" by our sin? And we are invited to respond.

Take a moment to journal your ideas, questions, or insights about this lesson. Write down thoughts you had that may not have been mentioned in the text or the discussion questions. List any personal applications you got from the lessons. What challenged you the most in the teachings? How might you turn what you've learned into specific action?

_____

_____

_____

_____

_____

_____

_____

_____

_____

_____

SESSION 4

SIGNS AND WONDERS

OPENING PRAYER

Come Holy Spirit,
fill the hearts of your faithful
and enkindle in them the fire of your love.
Send forth your Spirit
and they shall be created.
And you shall renew
the face of the earth.

Let us pray.
O, God, who did instruct
the hearts of the faithful
by the light of the Holy Spirit,
grant that by the same Holy Spirit
we may be truly wise
and ever rejoice in his consolation.
Through Christ our Lord.
Amen.

Sts. Peter and Paul, pray for us.

INTRODUCTION

In the last session we examined the importance of proclaiming the kerygma—the message of Jesus and the salvation that he offers—in the first evangelization. In this session we will look at how the Holy Spirit paved the way for the Apostles to proclaim the kerygma by performing signs and wonders through them and filling them with holy boldness to preach. These elements are still crucial to evangelization today. As the Acts of the Apostles demonstrates, evangelization is often met with opposition. Let's take a look and learn from the Apostles, who met this persecution not with fear, but with prayer for a renewed outpouring of the Holy Spirit.

CONNECT

Describe a time when you felt God calling you to step out in faith. How did you respond? And what happened?

What do you think is the most defining characteristic of a Christian?

DISCUSS

PART 1: HEALING OF THE LAME MAN
Watch the teaching on video. The following is a brief outline of the topics covered.

I. Signs and Wonders—Miracles Done
   Through the Apostles
   A. Signs, because they signify something else:
      reveal that Jesus is alive, his kingdom is here
   B. Wonders, because they cause wonder, awe,
      fear of the Lord

II. Healing of the Lame Man (Acts 3)
    A. 3 p.m. hour of prayer: hour of Jesus' Death,
       hour of evening sacrifice
    B. "gaze intently"—
    C. "In the name of Jesus Christ"; "raised him up"
       1. Jesus' Resurrection is the source of all
          the life he pours out on us
       2. Every healing is a prophecy of the
          Resurrection

E. First, act of faith; then, feet and ankles
    made strong

F. Isaiah 35:5-6 prophecies that the lame
   will leap

III. Peter Proclaims the Kerygma
   A. Jesus' name—brings his presence
      and authority
   B. Jesus can heal any time, but he chooses to
      involve his disciples (us)
   C. Number of believers grows significantly

DISCUSS

1. What is the relationship between performing signs and wonders and proclaiming the kerygma?

2. St. Luke tells us that St. Peter took the lame man by the hand and "raised him up." What is the deeper significance of this phrase?

3. Why does St. Peter place so much emphasis on the name of Jesus in his speech after healing the lame man? What application does this have for the New Evangelization?

PART 2: HOLY BOLDNESS
Watch the video teaching. The following is a brief outline of the topics covered.

I. Response of Priests (Acts 4)
    A. St. Peter responds with incredible boldness
    B. "Recognized that they had been with Jesus"
       (Acts 4:13; Mark 3:14-15)

II. Boldness *parrhesia* in Greek
    A. "With confidence" (Hebrews 4:16)
    B. "...filial trust, joyous assurance, humble
       boldness..." (CCC 2778)

III. First Persecution
    A. Pray for more boldness, more anointing
    B. Place is shaken, all filled with Holy Spirit

C. Renewed Pentecost—meant to happen again
and again   _____

D. Leads to Church expanding in next chapters   _____

_____

IV. Jesus Instructions (Matthew 10)   _____

A. We need to take every opportunity to fulfill
this command: offer to pray with others,   _____
lay hands on them while praying
                                                        _____
B. St. Francis Xavier—God does great works
through the simple and lowly   _____

DISCUSS

4. What does it mean to "be with Jesus"?

_____

_____

5. We are called to have boldness both in how we approach God in prayer and how we live out
and talk about our faith. Describe a time you have felt bold in prayer and a time you have felt
bold in your faith.

_____

_____

6. What role, if any, do you think signs and wonders have to play in the New Evangelization?

_____

_____

PART 3: LIBERTY FOR THE OPPRESSED
Watch the video teaching. The following is a brief outline of the topics covered.

I. Liberty for the Oppressed

A. After his baptism, Jesus proceeds to heal and
liberate, dismantling the kingdom/control of evil   _____

B. Church and Apostles also confront evil and
the oppressed   _____

_____

II. St. Paul in Philippi (Acts 16)   _____

A. Importance of discernment   _____

B. St. Paul expels/rebukes evil spirit
in Jesus' name   _____

C. This rouses strong opposition/persecution   _____

D. Persecution allows proclamation of kerygma   _____

III. Sons of Sceva Try to Capitalize on Jesus' Name _____
    (Acts 19)   _____
    A. Can't manipulate use of Jesus' name   _____
    B. Many give up evil practices   _____

IV. Deliverance: Part of the Church's Mission   _____
    A. Deliverance vs. exorcism   _____
    B. We have the Spirit of Jesus to resist Satan _____

DISCUSS

7. The examples of Jesus' life and the Acts of the Apostles indicate that we should expect opposition and even persecution in our mission. How does persecution become an opportunity for evangelization for St. Paul? When have you seen opposition or persecution turned into an opportunity for good?

_____

_____

8. In what ways have you witnessed or experienced the Church's mission of deliverance?

_____

_____

MEMORY VERSE

"Now when they saw the boldness of Peter and John, and perceived that they were uneducated, common men, they wondered; and they recognized that they had been with Jesus."

—**Acts 4:13**

CLOSING PRAYER

Lord Jesus,
you continually call us
to deeper faith and trust in you.
Please send us a renewal
of the anointing of your Holy Spirit,
and fill us with a holy boldness
to do your work and proclaim your name.
May we never forget
that everything we accomplish
is by your power and not ours,
and may our every word and deed
bring glory to you.
Amen.

Sts. Peter and Paul, pray for us

Peter and John heal a paralytic / Erich Lessing / Art Resource, NY

FOR FURTHER READING

Part Four: Christian Prayer in *The Catechism of the Catholic Church* (CCC 2558-2865).

Gallagher, Timothy, OMV, *The Discernment of Spirits: A Reader's Guide: An Ignatian Guide for Everyday Living.* The Crossroad Publishing Company, 2013.

Kreeft, Peter. Part Four: Questions about Demons in *Angels (and Demons).* San Francisco: Ignatius Press, 1995.

Neal Lozano, *Unbound: A Practical Guide to Deliverance.* Chosen Books, 2010

"I will call to mind the deeds of the LORD;
yea, I will remember thy wonders of old.
I will meditate on all thy work,
and muse on thy mighty deeds...
Thou art the God who workest wonders,
who hast manifested thy might among the peoples."
—Psalm 77:11–12, 14

We find signs and wonders scattered throughout all of salvation history. At each stage of the story, God has used miracles to show forth his glory and draw his people closer to himself. The story of God rescuing the Israelites from slavery in Egypt provides an excellent example of both the variety of signs and wonders as well as the purpose for which God performs these miracles in the Old Testament.

Moses is told that God will perform signs through him so that the Israelites "may believe that the LORD, the God of their fathers, the God of Abraham, the God of Isaac, and the God of Jacob, has appeared to [him]" (Exodus 4:5). The Exodus signs also demonstrate the power and majesty of the one true God to those who don't know (believe in) him. God promises to "multiply [his] signs and wonders in the land of Egypt" so that "the Egyptians shall know that [he is] the LORD" (Exodus 7:3, 5). The primary purpose of the ten plagues is the conversion of both Egypt and Israel.

After their exodus from Egypt, as each new crisis of faith arises for God's people as they wander in the desert, God performs new signs and wonders—giving water from the rock and manna to eat (Exodus 16:17)—to remind his people of who he is and to call them to faith. These miracles also demonstrate God's loving kindness as he cares for his people's physical and spiritual needs.

Crossing of the Red Sea / Scala / Art Resource, NY

Even after God establishes Israel in the Promised Land, he continues to perform signs and wonders through his prophets as one way to encourage the weak and call back those who are unfaithful. The prophet Elijah is a prime example of this. Read the account of Elijah's contest with the prophets of Baal on Mount Carmel in 1 Kings 18:19-40. What does Elijah proclaim as the purpose of the contest? When he prays, what reason does he give for why God should answer? What effect does the outcome of the contest have on the people?

_____

_____

Jesus healing the multitudes / HIP / Art Resource, NY

When we come to the many familiar miracles of Jesus' ministry, we find a striking continuity with the signs and wonders of the Old Testament. Just as God often used miracles to establish the credibility of his prophets in the Old Testament, the signs and wonders that Jesus performs demonstrate the truth of his claims about his identity: "The works which the Father has granted me to accomplish, these very works which I am doing, bear me witness that the Father has sent me" (John 5:36). These signs and wonders identify Jesus as the Messiah. In fact, when St. John the Baptist sends messengers to ask Jesus if he truly is the long-awaited Messiah, Jesus answers by referencing the miracles he has been performing (see Matthew 11:2–5; compare to Isaiah 35:4–6, Isaiah 42:5–9, and Isaiah 61:1–2).

Jesus' miracles are also physical signs demonstrating the more important spiritual healing that comes with faith and the forgiveness of sins. Jesus' miracles attract many to come and hear his teaching: "A multitude followed him, because they saw the signs which he did on those who were diseased" (John 6:2). Many, like the hemorrhaging woman, hear the reports of Jesus and his teaching and come to faith and are healed. Thus in the New Testament, as in the Old, miracles not only testify to who Jesus is and the truth of this teaching, but also assist in bringing people to conversion and faith.

Read Matthew 9:1-8. How does Jesus prove the reality of spiritual healing to the skeptical crowd?

_____

_____

Jesus promises his followers that those who believe in him will perform even greater signs and wonders than he himself had done (see John 14:12), and so it is no surprise that the Acts of the Apostles describes the early years of the Church as filled with miraculous healings, resurrections from the dead, rescues from prison, protections from dangers, and other signs and wonders. These miracles play an important part in the first evangelization, establishing continuity between Jesus and his Church, and confirming the truth of the Church's message.

The signs and wonders described in Scripture draw out a deep and consistent theme throughout the entire story of salvation history: God works miracles through those who believe in him in order to inspire faith. Down through the centuries, and even in our own day, God continues to work miracles through his saints and in the lives of his people. Just as it wasn't surprising to see miracles in the early years of the Church, so we shouldn't be surprised that these signs and wonders are especially prevalent today in places where the gospel is being preached and evangelization is being done for the first time, or the first time in many centuries, so as to bring about conversion and to inspire belief in the gospel of Jesus Christ.

COMMIT—DAY 2
BEING WITH JESUS

St. Paul tells us, "If anyone is in Christ, he is a new creation" (2 Corinthians 5:17). When a person comes to meet Jesus Christ and to spend time with him, he is changed.

> *"Now when they saw the boldness of Peter and John, and perceived that they were uneducated, common men, they wondered; and they recognized that they had been with Jesus."* —Acts 4:13

When Sts. Peter and John are put on trial before the Sanhedrin for preaching about Jesus, the Jewish authorities recognize that these men "had been with Jesus." It's not simply a matter of hearing their Galilean accent and recognizing their faces from the tumultuous events of Passover a few months prior—they recognize their association with Jesus primarily in the boldness and authority with which they speak. As Acts 4:13 says, the authorities clearly see Peter and John are common men lacking the formal education of religious teachers, and yet they are unafraid to teach the people and correct even the priests and the scribes.

Being with Jesus changes a person in a deep, dramatic way. Who is someone you know or have heard of who was recognizably changed by his or her encounter with Jesus? Would someone know, without being told, that you are a Christian? How?

_____

_____

Throughout the Gospels we see people encountering Jesus and walking away radically changed. One of the most striking examples is that of the Samaritan woman in John 4. She is a social outcast in her village, having had multiple husbands and then living with a man who isn't her husband. Her isolation is indicated by the fact that she comes to the well in the heat of the day by herself, rather than with the other women in the morning or evening. But after her conversation with Jesus, she rushes back to her village to invite everyone to come and see this man who just might be the Messiah. And, surprisingly, her neighbors listen to her. Rather than dismiss her as a sinner and an outcast, they let her lead them to Jesus. The people of her village saw something different in this woman after she had been with Jesus.

The evangelization of the ancient world was founded on this recognizable change in those who would be called "Christians." Everything they did was in the name of Jesus, and therefore in his presence and by his power. The early Christians continued to be with Jesus as they "devoted themselves to the apostles' teaching and fellowship, to the breaking of bread and the prayers" (Acts 2:42). In their fellowship and common prayer they remained in Christ, as he promised: "Where two or three are gathered in my name, there am I in the midst of them" (Matthew 18:20). Without this foundation of time spent with Jesus, there would have been no personal transformation and no successful evangelization in the early years of the Church. And, of course, the same is true today.

"Abide in me, and I in you. As the branch cannot bear fruit by itself, unless it abides in the vine, neither can you, unless you abide in me. I am the vine, you are the branches. He who abides in me, and I in him, he it is that bears much fruit, for apart from me you can do nothing."

—John 15:4–5

You've probably heard some version of the saying, "You can't give what you don't have." Any work of evangelization, parish project, or other religious endeavor that is not centered on the person of Jesus Christ will ultimately fail. And we will fail if we do not start that work by "being with Jesus." So how do we cultivate the practice of being with our Lord? How do we learn the habit of abiding in him so that our efforts may bear good fruit like the early Christians?

One way we deepen our abiding in Christ is through prayer.

"Prayer and Christian life are inseparable, for they concern the same love and the same renunciation, proceeding from love; the same filial and loving conformity with the Father's plan of love; the same transforming union in the Holy Spirit who conforms us more and more to Christ Jesus; the same love for all men, the love with which Jesus has loved us."

—CCC 2745

Blessed Teresa of Calcutta echoed this inseparable connection in a letter to her sisters and those in her order:

"Jesus wants me to tell you again, … how much love He has for each one of you—beyond all you can imagine. I worry some of you still have not really met Jesus—one to one—you and Jesus alone. We may spend time in chapel—but have you seen with the eyes of your soul how He looks at you with love? Do you really know the living Jesus—not from books but from being with Him in your heart? Have you heard the loving words He speaks to you? Ask for the grace, He is longing to give it. Until you can hear Jesus in the silence of your own heart, you will not be able to hear Him saying, 'I thirst' in the hearts of the poor. Never give up this daily intimate contact with Jesus as the real living person—not just the idea. How can we last even one day without hearing Jesus say, 'I love you'—impossible."

—Blessed Teresa of Calcutta, Letter, March 25, 1993

The more time we spend in Jesus' presence, sitting at his feet in prayer, the more fruitful Jesus will make our evangelization and work for his kingdom. Most laypeople don't have four hours a day to spend solely in prayer like Mother Teresa, but we can probably find a way to increase the time we spend being with Jesus in prayer little by little. How do you currently make time for prayer? What could you do to add something to your life of prayer?

_____

_____

_____

COMMIT—DAY 3
LECTIO: HEALING OF THE LAME MAN

The first of the signs and wonders recorded after Pentecost happens when Sts. Peter and John encounter a lame man on their way into the Temple. This event is a model of faith in action and of seizing the moment for evangelization. It is also a reminder that God cares for every detail of our lives and that he wants to use each of us to communicate that love and care to others.

St. Peter and St. John Healing a Lame Man at the Gate of the Temple / Image copyright © The Metropolitan Museum of Art. Image source: Art Resource, NY

LECTIO: The practice of praying with Scripture, *lectio divina*, begins with an active and close reading of the Scripture passage. Read the Scripture passage below and then answer the questions to take a closer look at some of the details of the passage.

"Now Peter and John were going up to the temple at the hour of prayer, the ninth hour. And a man lame from birth was being carried, whom they laid daily at that gate of the temple which is called Beautiful to ask alms of those who entered the temple. Seeing Peter and John about to go into the temple, he asked for alms. And Peter directed his gaze at him, with John, and said, 'Look at us.' And he fixed his attention upon them, expecting to receive something from them. But Peter said, 'I have no silver and gold, but I give you what I have; in the name of Jesus Christ of Nazareth, walk.' And he took him by the right hand and raised him up; and immediately his feet and ankles were made strong. And leaping up he stood and walked and entered the temple with them, walking and leaping and praising God. And all the people saw him walking and praising God, and recognized him as the one who sat for alms at the Beautiful Gate of the temple; and they were filled with wonder and amazement at what had happened to him. While he clung to Peter and John, all the people ran together to them in the portico called Solomon's, astounded."

—Acts 3:1-11

Where does this miracle occur?

_____

What does St. Peter do in this passage? What does St. John do? What is the lame man's response to being healed?

_____

_____

_____

How is the lame man's mobility described before and after St. Peter's command: "In the name of Jesus Christ of Nazareth, walk"?

_____

_____

How does the crowd in the Temple respond to the miracle?

_____

_____

> **MEDITATIO:** *Lectio*, a close reading and rereading, is followed by *meditatio*, time to reflect on the Scripture passage and to ponder the reason for particular events, descriptions, details, phrases, and even echoes from other Scripture passages that were noticed during *lectio*. Take some time now to meditate on the Scripture passage from page 71.

What range of emotions might the lame man have experienced as St. Peter grasped his hand and pulled him to his feet? Excitement at the prospect of healing? Fear that he would fall rather than walk? Faith inspired by Peter's authority and boldness? Recognition of the name of Jesus? Confusion? But at the moment his feet and ankles are made strong, all other thoughts or emotions are overcome by joy and thanksgiving. He leaped up and praised God, maybe using one of the psalms: "Make a joyful noise to the LORD, all the lands!...Come into his presence with singing! Know that the LORD is God!...Enter his gates with thanksgiving, and his courts with praise! (Psalm 100:1-4). The lame man received physical healing, and he and all those present in the temple courtyard heard the good news of Jesus Christ. The miracle caught their attention; the proclamation of the kerygma held it. They observed with amazement the wondrous sign; they received understanding in Peter's preaching. Peter's invocation of Jesus' name brought the power and presence of Jesus for a more miraculous healing—a healing from sin for those who believed and were baptized.

In Acts of the Apostles, St. Luke gives us specific details about this miracle's location— not just somewhere near the Temple, but at the Beautiful Gate. Acts is also clear that the people "recognized [the lame man] as the one who sat for alms at the Beautiful Gate of the temple." Why are these concrete details important for how signs and wonders help spread the gospel? How do they prepare the crowd for St. Peter's words? How do the concrete actions we do in our own lives prepare others to be receptive to the gospel message?

_____

_____

Imagine that you were among the crowd that day. What would have been your response? You can praise God along with the lame man or choose not to believe. Have you experienced God's healing power in your life—physically or spiritually? Have you seen healing in others' lives? What was your response?

_____

_____

In this passage only St. Peter's words are recorded, but St. John's presence is noted. What role do you think John plays in this event? What does this indicate about the importance of fellowship and community in mission and evangelization?

_____

_____

> **ORATIO, CONTEMPLATIO, RESOLUTIO:** Having read and meditated on today's Scripture passage, take some time to bring your thoughts to God (*oratio*) and engage God in silence (*contemplatio*). Then end your prayer by making a simple concrete resolution (*resolutio*) to respond to God's prompting of your heart in today's prayer.

_____

_____

_____

COMMIT—DAY 4
LIBERTY FOR THE OPPRESSED

Jesus on a sabbath on his way to a synagogue in Nazareth reading the book of Isaiah / Scala/White Images / Art Resource, NY

When Jesus began his public ministry, he did so with a very specific vision of what that ministry would look like and what it would accomplish. For this reason, he read a very specific passage when he stood up in the synagogue in Nazareth:

"The Spirit of the Lord GOD is upon me, because the LORD has anointed me to bring good tidings to the afflicted; he has sent me to bind up the brokenhearted, to proclaim liberty to the captives, and the opening of the prison to those who are bound; to proclaim the year of the LORD's favor, and the day of vengeance of our God; to comfort all who mourn."

—Isaiah 61:1–2

After reading this passage, Jesus said, "Today this scripture has been fulfilled in your hearing" (Luke 4:21). Not only was Jesus announcing the fulfillment of this prophecy in himself as the Messiah, but he was also announcing a new Jubilee year.

Read Leviticus 25:8-28. What different types of liberation and rest were accomplished by the Jubilee year? What spiritual symbolism do you see in these physical acts of release?

_____

_____

In the Old Testament, the Jubilee was a year of liberation, which God commanded the Israelites to celebrate every fiftieth year. The celebration was meant to recall the liberation of the Exodus and its blessings of freedom and restoration that God bestowed on his covenant people. Just as God liberated Israel from slavery in Egypt and brought them to the Promised Land, at each Jubilee year God's people were to liberate those among them who found themselves enslaved, in debt and estranged from their family land. Thus each new generation would experience God's liberating acts.

But God desired more than liberation from physical slavery; he desired his people's liberation from spiritual slavery—slavery to sin and the bondage that results from worshipping false gods. This release, this "year of the LORD's favor" promised by Isaiah, is what Jesus announces in the Nazareth synagogue, and it is what he accomplishes on the Cross, bringing about freedom from sin and Satan.

We can clearly see that Jesus views the devil and his spiritual slavery as the main enemy, because our Lord's first act after his Baptism is to go out in the wilderness to confront Satan. The shape of that confrontation gives us an important insight into the devil's tactics. Read the temptation narrative in Matthew 4:1-11. What kind of attacks does Satan make? What "weapon" does Jesus use to thwart these attacks?

_____

_____

Satan's attacks begin with, and are focused on, the identity of Jesus: "If you are the Son of God..." If the devil can get Jesus to doubt or forget his identity—to "compromise his filial attitude toward God," as the *Catechism* says (CCC 538)—then he can derail Christ's mission. Satan uses this same basic tactic against Christians in all ages of the Church. And while it rightly seems ludicrous to imagine Jesus forgetting that he is the Son of God, all too often we fall prey to this very attack; we forget our identity as God's beloved children, we let go of our trust in God's goodness, and we disobey and sin (see CCC 397).

It is this spiritual oppression, slavery to sin and the more serious demonic possession, from which Jesus liberates mankind. The Church continues Christ's ministry of liberty for the oppressed, first in her proclamation of the gospel and offering of the Sacraments of Baptism and Reconciliation, but also when she exercises her spiritual authority in a major exorcism. In the Acts of the Apostles, this ministry of liberation is carried out in very clear, visible ways. Not only do we hear of many receiving the forgiveness of sins in Baptism, but St. Paul casts out a demon from a slave girl in Philippi (Acts 16:16-18), and converts in Ephesus burn their books of magic (Acts 19:19). And Christianity has such an impact on the market for silver idols in Ephesus that the craftsmen of that city start a riot (Acts 19:21-40).

St. Paul at Ephesus / Album / Art Resource, NY

The early Christians encounter visible manifestations of the kingdom of darkness, and in Jesus' name they liberate those oppressed by the darkness. The Church does all of this today as well. She continues Jesus' ministry of exorcism, just as the Apostles did. She warns against the dangers of occult practices, even those that many consider harmless games, such as Ouija boards or Tarot cards. And she offers God's forgiveness and a safe haven to those who have been involved in such things.

But even though these more obvious manifestations of the kingdom of darkness persist in our modern world, more often we find ourselves facing spiritual oppression in disguise. The Church's ministry of liberation is not limited to those areas that are obviously spiritual; it extends to every type of oppression, including those that seem to be purely material. Anything that causes us to act against our dignity as children of the Father brings with it spiritual oppression. Abortion, pornography, excessive consumerism, substance abuse, and many other realities of our modern world hold countless people captive, waiting for the liberation only Jesus—and in his name the Church—can bring.

How can the Sacrament of Reconciliation address evil in our lives? How can it strengthen us to withstand the attacks of the devil?

_____

_____

_____

Curing the Crippled and the Resurrection of Tabitha, Masolino da Panicale. c. 1424–25
Brancacci Chapel, Church of Santa Maria del Carmine, Florence, Italy

Curing the Crippled and the Resurrection of Tabitha / Scala / Art Resource, NY

We return to Masolino's work in the Brancacci chapel, moving from the altar wall where last session's _St. Peter Preaching to the Multitude_ appears, to the right side wall. This wider space allows Masolino to combine two accounts from the Acts of the Apostles: on the left, St. Peter's healing of the lame man (Acts 3:1–10), and, on the right, the raising of Tabitha (Acts 9:36–43).

Where do these two events take place?

Healing of Lame Man (see Acts 3:1-2):

_____

Raising of Tabitha (see Acts 9:36-37):

_____

While these two events take place at different times and different locations, Masolino locates them both along a typical Tuscan street and piazza. The painting's linear perspective draws us into the background of the picture, where we see typical Florentine architecture. If we look closely, we see bird cages hanging in several windows, laundry hung over window sills to dry, window shutters partially opened or closed, a mother holding her young child by the hand as they walk in the piazza, and we are immediately at home and at ease in this everyday, familiar setting. But as we move from the background's ordinary setting into the events in the foreground, the extraordinary catches us by surprise.

As Sts. Peter and John walk to the Temple for prayer, they come across a man "lame from birth" asking for alms. We see this man on the left sitting on a low stool, facing Peter and John, his back to the viewer and extending his hand in his request for alms. St. Peter reaches out to the cripple, but his hand is empty—no money or material wealth to give—and St. Peter himself declares, "I have no silver and gold." But he continues: "In the name of Jesus Christ of Nazareth, walk."

Saint Peter healing cripple / Alfredo Dagli Orti / The Art Archive at Art Resource, NY

We are told that St. Peter took the man by the right hand and "raised him up." Masolino pictures the moment just ahead of Peter clasping the man's hand. Peter directs his gaze to the man, who in return looks earnestly up at Peter. We join the man's arrested gaze in anticipation of what will happen next. We do not see the man "walking and leaping," but if we had any doubts that Peter has the power to raise him up, we need only turn our gaze a little to the right.

As we cross the street in the painting, we move in time to the event in Acts 9 in Joppa, where Tabitha, a holy woman, "full of good works and acts of charity," has died. While Acts tells us that St. Peter is taken to an "upper room," Masolino keeps the event at street level opposite the healing of the cripple. We see the widows in the room, showing off the tunics and garments made by Tabitha (a show that would have resembled and highlighted the local Florentine textile work, especially in wool and silk).

Saint Peter healing cripple / Alfredo Dagli Orti / The Art Archive at Art Resource, NY

As with the healing of the lame man, there is no long theological discourse. St. Peter simply says, with authority, "Tabitha, rise." Masolino captures the moment "she opened her eyes, and when she saw Peter she sat up." Tabitha crosses her hands over her chest to receive Peter's priestly blessing as he appears to be departing into the street. The men in the room express the utter amazement at what has happened—their hands are raised and they look ready to jump back if only the room were larger.

The power of the Spirit working through St. Peter to raise Tabitha will certainly also make the lame man walk, such that he could stand up and join the two men walking down the street at the center of Masolino's painting. These two contemporary Florentine men provide a link not only between the two foreground miracles but also between the everyday life of the painting's background and us the viewer, such that we can easily imagine ourselves walking down the same street, about to pass these two finely dressed men. They are so engrossed in their conversation and the worries of the day that they don't even notice the miracles happening only a short distance away, and appear quite ready to walk on by.

The question for us is whether we too will walk on by, inattentive to the Spirit. Will we also allow temporal concerns to distract us from the work that the Spirit wants to do in our lives, and through us in the lives of others around us?

Take a moment to journal your ideas, questions, or insights about this lesson. Write down thoughts you had that may not have been mentioned in the text or the discussion questions. List any personal applications you got from the lessons. What challenged you the most in the teachings? How might you turn what you've learned into specific action?

_____

_____

_____

_____

_____

_____

_____

_____

_____

_____

SESSION 5

HOW JESUS MAKES AN EVANGELIST

OPENING PRAYER

Come Holy Spirit,
fill the hearts of your faithful
and enkindle in them the fire of your love.
Send forth your Spirit
and they shall be created.
And you shall renew
the face of the earth.

Let us pray.
O, God, who did instruct the hearts of the faithful
by the light of the Holy Spirit,
grant that by the same Holy Spirit
we may be truly wise
and ever rejoice in his consolation.
Through Christ our Lord.
Amen.

St. Philip, pray for us.

INTRODUCTION

The last session explored the important role played by signs and wonders in the first evangelization. This session will look at how Jesus commissions individuals to go out and do his work of evangelization. Through three examples from the book of Acts, we see a pattern of God choosing a variety of people in a variety of circumstances to be missionary disciples for his kingdom. By virtue of our Baptism, we have been commissioned for the same work, and the examples of the Ethiopian eunuch, Cornelius the centurion, and St. Paul will help us better understand the role we are called to play in evangelization.

CONNECT

How would you define the word "missionary"?

Think of a time you were chosen by someone else for a certain task or role. Would you have chosen that for yourself as well? How was the situation different because someone else chose you?

DISCUSS

PART 1: CONVERSION OF THE ETHIOPIAN EUNICH
Watch the teaching on video. The following is a brief outline of the topics covered.

I. Jesus Makes Us Missionary Disciples

II. Conversion of the Ethiopian Eunuch (Acts 8)
   A. God uses persecution to extend the gospel
   B. Eunuch, royal representative; in Jerusalem
      to worship the God of the Jews
   C. St. Philip attentive to God's direction in prayer
   D. 4th Suffering Servant Song (Isaiah 52:13–53:12)
   E. St. Philip proclaims the kerygma using
      Scripture, starting with Isaiah
   F. Eunuch's question
      1. "What is to prevent my being baptized?"—
      2. Isaiah 56:3-5—eunuchs included
   G. Eunuch becomes evangelist to Ethiopia
      (Psalm 68:31; 87:4; Zephaniah 3:10)

DISCUSS

1. What was one thing you heard for the first time or that was an "aha" moment for you?

_____

_____

2. St. Philip was attentive and obedient to the direction of the Holy Spirit. What are some things that we can do, as individuals and as communities, to foster a habit of listening for the promptings of the Spirit?

_____

_____

3. St. Philip meets the eunuch where he is, sharing a personalized evangelization rather than a one-size-fits-all proclamation of the Gospel. What are some things we can do to share the Good News in a way that addresses the individual needs of the people we encounter?

_____

_____

PART 2: CONVERSION OF PAUL THE PERSECUTOR
Watch the video teaching. The following is a brief outline of the topics covered.

I. Who Was This Man?   _____
    A. Saul—Jewish name; Paul—Roman name
    B. Roman citizen, born in Tarsus   _____
    C. Brilliant young Pharisee   _____
    D. Zealous Jew who persecuted the Church   _____

II. Journey to Damascus (Acts 9)   _____
    A. St. Paul's shock at meeting Jesus
    B. St. Paul calls him Lord; Old Testament title   _____
    C. "I am Jesus, whom you are persecuting"— _____
       Jesus is one with his followers
    D. St. Paul recognizes his sin, and God's mercy   _____
    E. The persecutor becomes a follower of Jesus   _____

III. In Damascus   _____
    A. Ananias gives perfect response of a disciple: _____
       "Here I am, Lord"
    B. Two important parts of St. Paul's mission   _____
       1. To bring the gospel to all nations
       2. This mission will include suffering   _____
    C. Literally and spiritually St. Paul regains   _____
       his sight; begins proclaiming the gospel

DISCUSS

4. What was one thing you heard for the first time or that was an "aha" moment for you?

_____

_____

5. How do you think Ananias felt when he was sent to St. Paul? How is his example important to us in the New Evangelization?

_____

_____

6. St. Paul begins preaching in the synagogues in Damascus immediately after his conversion. What does this tell us about Paul? How can we apply his example in our lives?

_____

_____

PART 3: CONVERSION OF CORNELIUS THE CENTURION
Watch the video teaching. The following is a brief outline of the topics covered.

I.   God Orchestrates Entrance of Gentiles
     into the Family of God
     A. Cornelius Gentile worshipper of God   _____
     B. Given vision about St. Peter   _____

II. St. Peter's Vision in Joppa (Acts 10)   _____
     A. St. Peter proclaims he has never eaten
        unclean foods   _____
     B. God's response: "What God has cleansed,
        you must not call common"   _____
     C. St. Peter realizes dietary laws symbolize
        the division between Jews and Gentiles.   _____

III. Cornelius's House   _____
     A. Cornelius gathers friends, repeats vision
     B. St. Peter proclaims the kerygma   _____
     C. Holy Spirit falls on all who hear—
     D. Another Pentecost, now for the Gentiles   _____
     E. "Can anyone forbid water for baptizing...?"
     F. This begins debate on whether circumcision   _____
        necessary for Gentile converts   _____

DISCUSS

7. What was one thing you heard for the first time or that was an "aha" moment for you?

_____

_____

8. In what ways does the coming of the Holy Spirit upon Cornelius and his household mirror Pentecost? In what ways is it different?

_____

_____

9. Cornelius gathers a crowd to hear St. Peter even before he knows that St. Peter will come. How can we imitate Cornelius's zeal for God and trust that God will show up and work?

_____

_____

MEMORY VERSE

"The grace of our Lord overflowed for me with the faith and love that are in Christ Jesus." —1 Timothy 1:14

CLOSING PRAYER

Lord Jesus,
you have called us to be missionary disciples
to carry your name
before the whole world,
just like St. Philip, the Ethiopian eunuch,
St. Paul, and St. Cornelius the centurion.
Teach us to always seek and obey your will.
Fill us with a deeper love for every member
of your Body, the Church.
And strengthen us in the face of suffering
that we may persevere
 to the glory of your name.
Amen.

St. Philip, pray for us.

FOR FURTHER READING

Gorman, Michael J. *Apostle of the Crucified Lord.* Grand Rapids: William B. Eerdmans, 2004. (Especially Chapter 1; "Paul's World(s)," Chapter 2; "Paul's Resumé," and Chapter 5; "Paul's Spirituality")

Weddell, Sherry A. *Forming Intentional Disciples: The Path to Knowing and Following Jesus.* Huntington, IN: Our Sunday Visitor, 2012.

Christ appearing to his disciples at the mount of Galilee / Scala / Art Resource, NY

COMMIT–DAY 1
JEWS AND GENTILES

The story of salvation history is a story of God choosing individuals, families, and even nations to be a means of blessing to the rest of mankind. We see this in the story of Abraham, where God promises that through Abraham's descendants the entire world will be blessed (Genesis 12:1-3). God doesn't single Abraham out for special blessings and then neglect the rest of humanity—he chooses Abraham for the sake of the rest of the world.

> *"Now therefore, if you will obey my voice and keep my covenant, you shall be my own possession among all peoples; for all the earth is mine, and you shall be to me a kingdom of priests and a holy nation. These are the words you shall speak to the children of Israel."*　　　　　—Exodus 19:5–6

Likewise when God sets apart the nation of Israel as his chosen people, his "own possession," and makes his covenant with them at Mount Sinai, he is both enlarging his covenant people (from the tribe of Abraham to the nation of Israel) and also preparing Israel to be a means of blessing to the other nations. Israel is blessed, and that blessing comes with responsibilities. Israel isn't meant to keep the gifts of the covenant and law to themselves. Israel's special status comes with the expectation that they will lead the other nations to God. They are the *first-born* son of God (Exodus 4:22), meant to set the example for the Gentiles, their younger brother nations.

After the Flood all of mankind was one family, but at the Tower of Babel sin broke that family apart as their language was confused and they were scattered abroad. Scripture, however, makes it clear that the nations would someday be reunited. Look up the following passages. What does each passage say about Israel (Judah) and/or the nations?

Look up:	What does it say about Israel (Judah) and/or the nations?
Genesis 49:10	
Psalm 68:31-32	
Psalm 98:4-9	
Isaiah 11:10	
Micah 4:1-2	
Zechariah 2:11	

Israel had a vital role to play is this reunification project. By living in accordance with the Law given at Mount Sinai, Israel was to be a mirror reflecting God to the nations and drawing the nations back to God. Unfortunately, more often the nations influenced Israel rather than the other way around. As Israel leaves Egypt they hold on tightly to Egyptian practices and idolatry (Exodus 32). When the Israelites encounter the Moabites on the edge of the Promised Land, they again prove how susceptible they are to foreign influence (Numbers 25:1-5). And even though God gives his people more specific (and restrictive) laws as a guide for how they are to live as his covenant people, many of Israel and Judah's kings allow and promote pagan idolatrous practices, including child sacrifice. (2 Kings 17:16-17)

The Martyrdom of the Seven Maccabee Brothers and their Mother / Image copyright © The Metropolitan Museum of Art. Image source: Art Resource, NY

Because of Israel's susceptibility to pagan practices, God gave his people laws to help protect them from pagan influence. These laws necessarily set them apart from their Gentile neighbors and limited any close association between the Jews and the nations around them (it's hard to share a meal when your religion forbids you from eating many of the foods common to another group of people). The divide between the Jews and the nations became even wider when Hellenism arrived in Palestine and Jews were faced with intense pressure, some even with mortal danger, to conform to Greek culture and religion (1 and 2 Maccabees). In the face of this oppression, many Jews came to view the Gentiles as not only "not Jewish" but as inherently sinful and evil because of their idolatry and immorality.

While the Jews still understood themselves as the Chosen People, their role as a light to the nations was all but forgotten, with the small exception of those Gentile converts who were willing to fully embrace the Mosaic Law and be circumcised and only then were allowed to participate as full members of God's covenant people. But Christ, who is the light of the world (John 8:12), redeems Israel's failure. And his Church, directed by the Holy Spirit working through Christ's missionary disciples, brings to fulfillment the prophecies concerning Jew and Gentile worshipping God together. In the New Covenant we are not governed by a protective law of separation but by the law of the Spirit, which calls us to be the salt of the earth and the light of the world (Matthew 5:13-14).

What are some practical things that we can do to be present and involved in the world around us in order to evangelize, but still protect ourselves from the negative influences of the world?

_____

_____

_____

The Light of the World / HIP / Art Resource, NY

"This is the law pertaining to beast and bird and every living creature that moves through the waters and every creature that swarms upon the earth, to make a distinction between the unclean and the clean and between the living creature that may be eaten and the living creature that may not be eaten." —Leviticus 11:46-47

Acts 10 is a major turning point in salvation history. For nearly all of Israel's history there had been a sharp distinction between God's Chosen People and the nations, as described in Commit—Day 1. The conversion of Cornelius, and God's outpouring of the Spirit upon him and his household, announces to the Church as St. Peter observed to the circumcision party that, "the Spirit told me to go with them, making no distinction" (Acts 11:12). As St. Paul would later observe, "God shows no partiality" (Romans 2:11). The Holy Spirit makes Jews and Gentiles equal heirs of salvation.

As the leader of the Apostles and head of the Church, St. Peter receives the message that "what God has cleansed, you must not call common" (Acts 10:15). Consider the laws concerning clean and unclean animals in Leviticus 11, and especially the reason God gives for maintaining these distinctions in verses 44-45. How does God use the dietary laws of the Torah as an allegory to teach St. Peter that the division between Jew and Gentile is being overcome?

_____

_____

The Israelites had lived with the Mosaic dietary laws for their entire history as a nation. Like many of the laws given through Moses after the golden calf, the dietary restrictions were meant to be a safeguard to protect the Israelites from pagan influence (see Galatians 3:19-25 for the law as a custodian). These laws had a specific and necessary purpose, but the distinctions between clean and unclean did not indicate an inherent good or evil in the foods themselves.

Look up God's covenant with Noah in Genesis 9:1–4. What does God have to say about dietary restrictions here?

_____

_____

The most obvious implication of St. Peter's vision—that the Mosaic dietary laws are not binding on Gentile Christians—would be an important revelation for Christians. But the meaning of Peter's vision goes beyond the Mosaic Law's distinction between clean and unclean foods, as Peter quickly realizes with the immediate arrival of St. Cornelius's messengers.

Acts describes Cornelius as "a devout man who feared God with all his household, gave alms liberally to the people, and prayed constantly to God" (Acts 10:2). He is a Gentile who worships the God of the Jews but has not been circumcised. In the ancient world these Gentile admirers of Judaism were referred to as God-fearers (Acts 13:16, 26) or fearers of Heaven (in Jewish sources such as the Palestinian Talmud and Josephus). They worshipped with the Jews in their synagogues and followed many of the precepts of Judaism, but they were not full members of the covenant people because they did not receive circumcision. (The Ethiopian eunuch in Acts 8 is another example of a God-fearer.)

> *"And when a stranger shall sojourn with you and would keep the Passover to the LORD, let all his males be circumcised, then he may come near and keep it; he shall be as a native of the land. But no uncircumcised person shall eat of it."* —Exodus 12:48

> *"No foreigner, uncircumcised in heart and flesh, of all the foreigners who are among the people of Israel, shall enter my sanctuary."* —Ezekiel 44:9

Because God-fearers were not circumcised, they could not participate in the Passover meal and they could not pass beyond the Court of the Gentiles in the Temple in Jerusalem. So although they abandoned idolatry and observed many aspects of the Law, they were not full members of the covenant people. They remained separated from the Jews in the most important aspects of liturgical worship: the Temple and the Passover.

Peter in the House of Cornelius, drawings by Gustave Dore © Nicku / shutterstock.com

While St. Peter is still preaching the gospel of Jesus Christ to Cornelius and his household, God pours out his Spirit, to the amazement of those who traveled with Peter. Peter's question, "Can any one forbid water for baptizing these people who have received the Holy Spirit just as we have?" (Acts 10:47), announces to his Jewish-Christian companions that this liturgical exclusion is now at an end. Now in the Church, the former foreigners and outsiders are on equal footing. It wouldn't be an easy transition for all, for as we have seen the Jews had grown accustomed to being completely set apart from the nations, and many Jewish Christians held tight to the old law and distinctions. The Jerusalem Council (Acts 15) would have to address the question of whether Gentile converts could become Christians and participate in the Eucharist, the new Passover, without being circumcised and adhering to the full Mosaic law.

Despite the cultural and religious divide between Jews and Gentiles, and his initial perplexity at the vision he was given, St. Peter was attentive to the Holy Spirit and went to Cornelius "without objection" when he was invited (Acts 10:29). He cooperated fully with God's call to evangelize the Gentiles, and in doing so recognized the full meaning of the vision. In our own lives we may find God calling us to share the Gospel in unexpected places and with unexpected people. What can we do to truly live out the truth that Peter recognized, that "God shows no partiality" (Acts 10:34)?

COMMIT–DAY 3
LECTIO: CONVERSION
OF THE ETHIOPIAN EUNUCH

Have you ever wished God would just tell you what you were supposed to do next? Or, better yet, simply whisk you away and deposit you right where you are supposed to be? In Acts 8, St. Philip experiences exactly this as God directs him to one evangelization opportunity after another. Although we might not audibly hear an angel tell us what to do or experience miraculous relocation, we can strive to imitate Philip's example of prayerful preparation, ready obedience, and bold proclamation.

Landscape with St Philip baptizing the eunuch / HIP / Art Resource, NY

> **LECTIO:** The practice of praying with Scripture, *lectio divina*, begins with an active and close reading of the Scripture passage. Read the Scripture passage below and then answer the questions to take a closer look at some of the details of the passage.

"But an angel of the Lord said to Philip, 'Rise and go toward the south to the road that goes down from Jerusalem to Gaza.' This is a desert road. And he rose and went. And behold, an Ethiopian, a eunuch, a minister of Candace, queen of the Ethiopians, in charge of all her treasure, had come to Jerusalem to worship and was returning; seated in his chariot, he was reading the prophet Isaiah. And the Spirit said to Philip, 'Go up and join this chariot.' So Philip ran to him, and heard him reading Isaiah the prophet, and asked, 'Do you understand what you are reading?' And he said, 'How can I, unless some one guides me?' And he invited Philip to come up and sit with him. Now the passage of the Scripture which he was reading was this: 'As a sheep led to the slaughter or a lamb before its shearer is silent, so he opens not his mouth. In his humiliation justice was denied him. Who can describe his generation? For his life is taken up from the earth.' And the eunuch said to Philip, 'About whom, pray, does the prophet say this, about himself or about some one else?' Then Philip opened his mouth, and beginning with this Scripture he told him the good news of Jesus. And as they went along the road they came to some water, and the eunuch said, 'See, here is water! What is to prevent my being baptized?' And he commanded the chariot to stop, and they both went down into the water, Philip and the eunuch, and he baptized him. And when they came up out of the water, the Spirit of the Lord caught up Philip; and the eunuch saw him no more, and went on his way rejoicing. But Philip was found at Azotus, and passing on he preached the gospel to all the towns till he came to Caesarea." —Acts 8:26–40

In what ways does God direct St. Philip? How does he respond?

_____

_____

How does St. Philip begin his evangelization? What does this tell us about his approach to preaching the gospel?

_____

_____

How does the eunuch respond to St. Philip's initial question? To his proclamation of the Gospel? To Baptism?

_____

_____

MEDITATIO: *Lectio*, a close reading and rereading, is followed by *meditatio*, time to reflect on the Scripture passage and to ponder the reason for particular events, descriptions, details, phrases, and even echoes from other Scripture passages that were noticed during *lectio*. Take some time now to meditate on the Scripture passage from page 89.

Consider the beautiful example of St. Philip's obedience in this passage. Philip responds immediately to the Lord's instruction to go to the Gaza road—even though he isn't told why he is supposed to go or what he is supposed to do there. He doesn't insist on having the big picture; he simply obeys. While it is nice to know the details or the final goal of the work God has for us, often God wants us to obey first so that we grow in our trust of him. When it is time for the next step, God will make it clear, as he does for Philip: "Go up and join this chariot."

Consider the beautiful example of the eunuch's humility in this passage. He is a powerful government official in charge of the wealth of the Ethiopian queen. He is traveling in a royal chariot and with his own copy of Isaiah to read. He is well-educated, reading the Scriptures of another nation. And yet, when he is approached by a stranger of a lower social class who asks him, "Do you understand?" the eunuch admits that he is in need of instruction. Because of his humility and desire for understanding, he opens the door of his chariot to St. Philip, who with his preaching will open the door to true wisdom and knowledge in Jesus Christ.

Imagine the joy of both of these men at their Spirit-led encounter: the eunuch, realizing that he can be baptized and finally enter fully into God's covenant, and St. Philip, reaping the harvest of this new Christian who will go home and sow the seeds of the Gospel. We can foster the same prayerful openness and rapid obedience to the will of God. We can learn the same humility in the face of our own limitations. We can experience and share the same joy of the Gospel.

St. Philip is readily obedient to God's directions in this passage. In your own life, what has the potential to get in the way of obedience to God's will? How can you overcome this?

_____

_____

The eunuch clearly longs for a deeper understanding of the Scriptures, and he is not afraid to admit his lack of knowledge and ask for instruction. What is one area of your faith life where you need some help? To whom can you turn for assistance?

_____

_____

St. Philip's evangelization is based in Scripture: He begins his proclamation of the Gospel using the passage from Isaiah the eunuch is reading at that moment. What Scriptures would you include in explaining the message of Jesus Christ to someone?

_____

_____

_____

ORATIO, CONTEMPLATIO, RESOLUTIO: Having read and meditated on today's Scripture passage, take some time to bring your thoughts to God (*oratio*) and engage God in silence (*contemplatio*). Then end your prayer by making a simple concrete resolution (*resolutio*) to respond to God's prompting of your heart in today's prayer.

_____

_____

_____

_____

_____

St. Philip baptizing the Queen of Ethiopia's eunuch on the road from Jerusalem to Gaza / © RMN-Grand Palais / Art Resource, NY

COMMIT—DAY 4
ST. PAUL, GOD'S EVANGELIST

Saint Paul paint from Paris - St. Severin church © Renata Sedmakova / shutterstock.com

St. Paul is one of the giants of the early Church. His writings make up nearly one-quarter of the New Testament. He traveled extensively on his three missionary journeys and earned the title "Apostle to the Gentiles" for his untiring dedication to spreading the Gospel. But before Paul was such an important figure in Christianity, he was a rising star in first-century Judaism. And St. Paul's first encounters with the Church were quite the opposite of the work for which he has been known and admired throughout history.

St. Paul, also known as Saul, was born in the town of Tarsus, the capital of the Roman province of Cilicia (located near the southern coast of modern-day Turkey). Tarsus was famous in the ancient world for its university specializing in rhetoric. Paul was from the tribe of Benjamin and his father was a Roman citizen, and so he was both a faithful Jew and a Roman citizen. His Roman citizenship meant that he had certain legal rights other Jews didn't necessarily have, such as protection from being punished without a trial (Acts 22:25-29).

"Saul, who is also called Paul" (Acts 13:19)—It was common for first-century Jews to have both a Hebrew and a Greek (or Latin) name. As a Pharisee and student of the law, Saul goes by his Hebrew name, after the first king of Israel (also a Benjaminite). After his conversion and his commissioning as apostle to the Gentiles, it makes sense that he would go by his Roman/Latin name, Paul—especially as "Saul" in Greek (*saulos*) was used to refer to the style of walking of some prostitutes.

St. Paul moved from Tarsus to Jerusalem, where he became a Pharisee and a student of the famous rabbi Gamaliel. In his zeal for God's law, Paul perceived the Christians to be a dangerous threat to Judaism. Though still a young man, he was quickly rising to a position of authority, which he used to try to stop this threat.

We first encounter St. Paul at the martyrdom of St. Stephen: "Then they cast him out of the city and stoned him; and the witnesses laid down their garments at the feet of a young man named Saul.... And Saul was consenting to his death" (Acts 7:58, 8:1). Paul wasn't just the young student watching over the cloaks while the older men carried out Stephen's execution—these details indicate that Paul was the authority authorizing the stoning of Stephen. Paul's privileged position is confirmed in Acts 9:1-2, when he goes directly to the high priest to obtain letters to the synagogues in Damascus authorizing him to arrest the followers of "the Way."

St. Paul's position regarding Christianity illustrates the difference between knowledge and understanding. He had received a first-rate education in the Law and the Prophets, and he had knowledge of the claims of Christianity. But he didn't yet have understanding to make the necessary connections and see the truth of "the Way." It is only when he encounters Jesus himself, is baptized, and receives the Holy Spirit that Paul is able to understand and say "Jesus is Lord" (1 Corinthians 12:3).

Read the account of St. Paul's conversion in Acts 9:1-19. How do you think he felt when he realized that he had been persecuting the Lord he claimed to serve, rather than a band of dangerous heretics? What might he have been thinking about during his three days of darkness before Ananias came to him?

_____

_____

_____

During those days of darkness, St. Paul likely recalled St. Stephen's martyrdom. Stephen's words recounting many great men and events of salvation history—Abraham, Jacob, Joseph, Moses, Mount Sinai, Solomon, the Temple, the prophets—must have echoed over and over again in Paul's mind, forcing him to see them in a new light, in the bright light of Jesus Christ. Perhaps he recalled Stephen's face as he, "full of the Holy Spirit, gazed into heaven and saw the glory of God" (Acts 7:55). Paul might also have considered Stephen's last words as he was stoned to death: "Lord, do not hold this sin against them" (Acts 7:60). This prayer of the first Christian martyr for mercy on those who persecuted him is answered only two chapters later by the conversion of the most fervent enemy of the Church. Stephen's martyrdom brought a flood of mercy and grace, not only on Paul, but also through Paul to each of those who would receive the Gospel by his preaching.

The stoning of St. Stephen / HIP / Art Resource, NY

It isn't easy to pray for our enemies, but it is both necessary (Matthew 5:44) and extremely powerful. Who is in need of your prayers of forgiveness and mercy today?

_____

COMMIT—DAY 5
TRUTH AND BEAUTY

The Conversion of St. Paul, Caravaggio, 1601 Cerasi Chapel,
Church of Santa Maria del Popolo, Rome, Italy

The Conversion of Saint Paul / Restored Tradition Art

Imagine yourself as a medieval pilgrim. You have saved money for years to make a pilgrimage to
Rome. You have traveled on foot from Spain, or France, walking for months in order to pray at the
holy sites of the Eternal City. You finally arrive at the City of Martyrs and enter the first church you
see inside the city walls, the Church of Santa Maria del Popolo. You stop in awe before Caravaggio's
paintings of *The Conversion of St. Paul* and the *Crucifixion of St. Peter,* both displayed in the church's
Cerasi side chapel. You have come to Rome to see the tombs of Sts. Peter and Paul, the founders
of the Church in Rome; now you are confronted with the scenes of St. Paul's conversion and St.
Peter's martyrdom. After praying before these images, you bring the fruit of your meditation on

conversion and martyrdom with you as you make your pilgrimage through Rome, visiting the holy sites and allowing God's grace to bring you to deeper conversion and prepare you to lay down your own life, even to the point of martyrdom if necessary.

St. Paul, the subject of this painting, was the greatest evangelist in history. Everything about Paul, previously called Saul, was intense, from his accomplishments as a brilliant young Jewish scholar to the ferocity with which he virulently persecuted the new sect that followed the crucified Jesus. It would seem that capturing the attention of this man as he was "breathing murderous threats" against Christians would necessitate a grand event. His conversion was just that. Caravaggio does justice to this dramatic encounter between Jesus and Saul, using intense and even violent gestures to demonstrate the action in this work. The painter portrays the decisive moment from the account of Saul's conversion, when ashed about him and he hears God's voice calling, "Saul, Saul."

The Conversion of Saint Paul / Restored Tradition Art

Saul has just been thrown from his horse, arms outstretched as he falls to the ground. Eyes closed, he seems to be in the midst of a revelation. The intensity of emotion and drama depicted draws the viewer into the painting, allowing him to participate in the event. We are not meant to be passive viewers of this work.

Notice how Caravaggio uses every bit of available space—the figures are practically bursting the bounds of the canvas, as if coming out of the frame to us. The viewer, at eye level with St. Paul, would feel his body almost breaking through the bottom of the painting, coming into our space and reminding us that the conversion of Paul and the events of Scripture are not just merely historical events. They are part of our story, and we are to participate in them, to meditate on them, and to allow Jesus to bring us to conversion through consideration of them.

Caravaggio, known for his *chiaroscuro* technique (in Italian *chiaro* means light and *scuro*, darkness), uses light and darkness in a striking and original way. Light has a particular significance in Christian thought and the Scriptures. Look up the following Scriptures and note how light is described:

Psalm 119:105 _____

Job 33:30 _____

Matthew 4:16 _____

John 1:4-5 _____

Light is charged with symbolism, representing illumination and the revelation of God's Word. Moreover, prophetic writers, particularly Isaiah, describe Israel as a "light to the nations" (Isaiah 49:6). Jesus does not merely use this image as a metaphor to describe himself, but he also identifies himself with it: "I am the light of the world" (John 8:12; 9:5). Caravaggio uses light in a particular way, in a way that manifests this Christian understanding. Caravaggio utilizes light to represent the supernatural, which overcomes the darkness. The great drama of good versus evil, light versus darkness, Caravaggio exploits to the full in his religious paintings.

Caravaggio's solid, and very much three-dimensional, figures are enhanced by the strong light that falls on them. He uses light to isolate and to direct the viewer's attention. We see the light on the fallen Saul, but we do not see its source. The focus is on Saul's experience of that light, of his heavenly vision. He sees a flash of light and hears the voice of the Lord, but he is struck blind for three days, symbolizing the state of his soul before this revelation. Only by the gift of the Holy Spirit, who leads to the light of truth, given at the laying on of Ananias' hands, will St. Paul regain his sight. Caravaggio allows us to be bathed in this heavenly light that dispels the darkness of Saul's soul, giving him the light of life.

Having experienced firsthand the light of God's revelation, St. Paul also uses the image of light in his writings. Look up the following passages from his letters. How does Paul use the image of light?

Ephesians 5:13-14 _____

Romans 2:19 _____

Romans 13:12 _____

Colossians 1:12 _____

Take a few moments to meditate on Caravaggio's *The Conversion of St. Paul*, calling to mind St. Paul's words: "For it is the God who said, 'Let light shine out of darkness,' who has shone in our hearts to give the light of the knowledge of the glory of God in the face of Christ" (2 Corinthians 4:6), and thanking God for the light that he has shone in your heart and life.

_____

_____

_____

_____

SESSION 6

SACRAMENTS AND THE SPIRIT

OPENING PRAYER

Come Holy Spirit,
fill the hearts of your faithful
and enkindle in them the fire
of your love.
Send forth your Spirit
and they shall be created.
And you shall renew the face of the earth.

Let us pray.
O, God, who did instruct
the hearts of the faithful
by the light of the Holy Spirit,
grant that by the same Holy Spirit
we may be truly wise
and ever rejoice in his consolation.
Through Christ Our Lord.
Amen.

Holy Apostles, pray for us.

INTRODUCTION

In the last session, we considered how Jesus transforms ordinary people into evangelists or missionary disciples. Now let's examine what the Acts of the Apostles tells us about how new believers in Christ were initiated into the early Church. In this session, we turn to the Sacraments of Initiation—Baptism, Confirmation, and Eucharist—to see how they are evident from the beginnings of Christian evangelization. We will discover how these three sacraments conveyed, sustained, and energized the new life in the Spirit for these early Christians and how the power of these sacraments still flows through the Church today.

CONNECT

Have you ever been initiated into a group, such as citizenship of a particular country, a special club, or a sorority or fraternity? How did the rites or activities reflect your initiation into the group?

Have you ever felt called to do something that you did not feel equipped to handle by yourself? What was the task, and how did you overcome your feelings of inadequacy to complete it?

DISCUSS

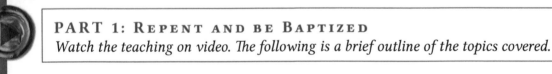

PART 1: REPENT AND BE BAPTIZED
Watch the teaching on video. The following is a brief outline of the topics covered.

I. Sacraments of Initiation: Baptism, Confirmation, Eucharist
  A. Repent and be baptized
    1. Pentecost gift of Spirit to be perpetuated
    2. Free gift given through the Church

II. What Happens When Baptized?
  A. Buried with Christ (Romans 6)
  B. Old and New Testament events
    1. Flood; new beginning through water
    2. Exodus; exodus from sin to new life in God
    3. Jesus' baptism
  C. Early Church accounts/testimony—St. Cyprian
    1. To bring the gospel to all nations
    2. This mission will include suffering
    3. Expectation of charisms
    4. Baptism's effect often differs from subjective experience

III. Infant Baptism   _____
    A. Promise not only to you, but to your children
    B. Lydia—"whole household"; jailer—   _____
       "with all his family"   _____

DISCUSS

1. At Pentecost, God poured out his Spirit on the disciples. What is the purpose of this gift, and for whom is it meant? How is it shared?

_____

_____

2. Baptism is more than a rite of passage; it is a very real and radical transformation. What do Scripture and the early Church Fathers tell us about the manifested effects of Baptism in the early Church? How can we prepare catechumens (converts to the faith preparing for Baptism) to expect a similar experience at their baptism?

_____

_____

3. Why do Catholics baptize infants (see Acts 2:39)? Look up the following verses and describe how each supports the practice of infant baptism.

Acts 16:15 _____

Acts 16:33 _____

Acts 18:8 _____

PART 2: THE LAYING ON OF HANDS
Watch the video teaching. The following is a brief outline of the topics covered.

I. Philip Heads to Samaria (Acts 8)   _____
    A. Many baptized, but something missing
    B. Spirit had not yet fallen on these newly baptized _____
    C. Apostles concerned that all new converts receive _____
       fullness of the Spirit they received at Pentecost
    D. Simon Magician (simony—buying or selling   _____
       spiritual things)   _____

II. Confirmation   _____
    A. "Effect...outpouring of the Holy Spirit
       as once granted to the apostles" (CCC 1302-1303) _____
       1. Divine filiation; know the Father in a new way _____
       2. Unites us more firmly to Christ   _____

3. Increases gifts of Holy Spirit in us

4. More perfect bond with the Church   _____

5. Strengthened to spread and defend the Faith   _____

6. Confess the name of Christ boldly

7. Never ashamed of the Cross   _____

   B. Often a "gap" between what is experienced   _____

III. Baptism and Full Gift of the Spirit Are Necessary   _____

Discuss

4. What happened when Philip went down to Samaria and preached the Word of God (see Acts 8:4-8)? What is so significant about Philip preaching to the Samaritans?

_____

_____

5. Why did the Apostles send Peter and John down to Samaria? What did the Apostles want to accomplish? What do we learn about God's gifts from the episode with Simon the magician (see Acts 8:18-24)?

_____

_____

6. Pick one effect of the outpouring of the Holy Spirit (see CCC1302-1303) and discuss how it can help make us missionary disciples. Which of these effects of the Holy Spirit would you like to experience more in your own life? Why?

_____

_____

PART 3: THE BREAKING OF BREAD
Watch the video teaching. The following is a brief outline of the topics covered.

I. "Devoted to Breaking of Bread" (Acts 2:42)

  A. Full communal life centered on   _____
     "breaking of the bread"   _____

  B. Table fellowship now with people never   _____
     associated with before   _____

  C. Powerful bond of unity (1 Corinthians 10:16-17)   _____

  D. Eucharist and Church are Body of Christ;   _____
     not unrelated and not just metaphors   _____

  E. "Be members then of the Body of Christ that   _____
     your Amen may be true...be then what you see   _____
     and receive then what you are."   _____
          —St. Augustine, Sermon 272   _____

II. Troas (Acts 20)
    A. Eucharist celebrated on Sunday, day of
       Resurrection, first day of the week
    B. Eutychus raised; sign of the power
       of the Eucharist in us

III. Early Church Process of Initiation
    A. First, heard about Jesus or witnessed signs
    B. Time of catechumenate; up to 3 years
    C. Initiation typically culminated at Easter Vigil
       liturgy—baptized, confirmed, Eucharist

IV. Eucharist Source/Culmination
    of Evangelization
    A. Source—Receiving Jesus impels us outward
    B. Culmination—lead others into full communion

DISCUSS

7. How does the Eucharist bring about the unity Paul describes in Galatians 3:28: "You are all one in Christ Jesus"? Why was this so astounding?

_____

_____

8. How is the Eucharist the source and culmination of evangelization? How do you experience this in your own life?

_____

_____

MEMORY VERSE

"We were buried therefore with him by baptism into death, so that as Christ was raised from the dead by the glory of the Father, we too might walk in newness of life." —Romans 6:4

CLOSING PRAYER

A Prayer to the Holy Spirit prayed by Pope St. John Paul II from his childhood:

Holy Spirit, I ask you for the gift of Wisdom
to better know You and Your divine perfections,
for the gift of Understanding to clearly discern the spirit
of the mysteries of the holy faith,
for the gift of Counsel that I may live according
to the principles of this faith,
for the gift of Knowledge that I may look for counsel
in You and that I may always find it in You,
for the gift of Fortitude that no fear
or earthly preoccupations
would ever separate me from You,
for the gift of Piety that I may always serve Your Majesty
with a filial love,
for the gift of Fear of the Lord that I may dread sin,
which offends You, O my God.
Amen.

Holy Apostles, pray for us.

The Holy Trinity Gianni Dagli Orti / The Art Archive at Art Resource, NY

FURTHER READING

Paragraphs on the Sacraments of Christian Initiation in the *Catechism of the Catholic Church*: 1212-1419

Pope St. John Paul II, *Dominum et Vivificantem (On the Holy Spirit in the Life of the Church and the World)*, no. 25-26

COMMIT—DAY 1
BAPTISM

When we gather around the baptismal font to witness the Baptism of an infant dressed in white, we think of "new life" and "rebirth"—and rightly so. Yet St. Paul can speak of Baptism, saying: "Do you not know that all of us who have been baptized into Christ Jesus were baptized into his death? We were buried therefore with him by baptism into death" (Romans 6:3-4). Death and rebirth...this paradox is a mystery central to our faith and at the heart of Baptism.

Scripture helps us understand this paradox. What do these verses tell us about what happens in baptism?

Little girl on ceremony of child christening in church © mylu / shutterstock.com

John 3:5 _____

Colossians 2:11-13 _____

1 Peter 3:18-21 _____

That Baptism includes both death (a death to sin) and new life (life in the Spirit) is clear as St. Paul continues: "...so that as Christ was raised from the dead by the glory of the Father, we too might walk in newness of life" (Romans 6:4). Baptism is the sacrament of new life, "the regeneration through water in the word" (CCC 1213). Through Baptism, all sins are forgiven, the stain of Original Sin is washed clean, and new life is given by the indwelling of the Blessed Trinity in the soul of the baptized. As the *Catechism* states, "Through Baptism we are freed from sin and reborn as sons of God" (CCC 1213). We receive sanctifying grace, and our souls are imprinted with an indelible mark that identifies us as God's own. We become sons and daughters of the King and therefore heirs to eternal life with him in Heaven.

Because of our death to sin and incorporation into God's family, the story of God's mighty deeds throughout salvation history becomes "our story." The Church recalls many of these deeds and events as part of her baptismal liturgy, reminding us how God's actions in salvation history pointed forward toward this Baptism into new life. We can see this by taking a look at several of the stanzas in the prayer of blessing of the baptismal water used at the Easter Vigil Liturgy.

Easter Vigil Blessing of Baptismal Water: (Roman Missal, Easter Vigil, 46)	Connection to Baptism:
O God, who by invisible power *accomplish a wondrous effect* *through sacramental signs* *and who in many ways* *have prepared water, your creation,* *to show forth the grace of Baptism;*	At the Creation, God created the world *ex nihilo*, out of nothing (see Genesis 1:1). In a similar way it is God's "invisible power" that makes a new creation in the one baptized.
O God, whose Spirit *in the first moments of the world's creation* *hovered over the waters,* *so that the very substance of water* *would even then take to itself the power to sanctify;*	The power of the Spirit moved over the waters at Creation (see Genesis 1:2). In Baptism, it is the power of the Holy Spirit that gives natural water the power to effect a supernatural change (the forgiveness of sins and the incorporation into the family of God) in the one being baptized.
O God, who by the outpouring of the flood *foreshadowed regeneration,* *so that from the mystery* *of one and the same element of water* *would come an end to vice and a beginning* *of virtue;*	The waters of the flood washed away the evil and wickedness that was upon the earth, and God started again with the righteous family of Noah (Genesis 6:5-9). Similarly, Baptism's water washes away sin and gives us the grace to live in imitation of Christ, the Righteous One.
God, who caused the children of Abraham *to pass dry-shod through the Red Sea,* *so that the chosen people,* *set free from the slavery of Pharaoh,* *would prefigure the people of the baptized;*	In the Exodus, God's people passed through the waters of the Red Sea and were saved from slavery (Exodus 14:21-31). In Baptism we are set free from slavery to sin.
O God, whose Son, *baptized by John in waters of the Jordan,* *was anointed with the Holy Spirit,* *and, as he hung upon the Cross,* *gave forth water from his side along with blood,* *and after his Resurrection, commanded his disciples:* *"Go forth, teach all nations, baptizing them* *in the name of the Father and of the Son and* *of the Holy Spirit,"* *look now, we pray, upon the face of your Church* *and graciously unseal for her the fountain* *of Baptism.*	It is because of Jesus' command that the Apostles baptized all new believers, and that the Church continues this practice to the present day. The same Spirit that anointed Jesus at his Baptism in the Jordan anoints us and incorporates us into Christ.

Looking forward to the promise of eternal life made possible through Baptism, the final stanza concludes:

> *May this water receive by the Holy Spirit*
> *the grace of your Only Begotten Son,*
> *so that human nature, created in your image*
> *and washed clean through the Sacrament of Baptism*
> *from all the squalor of the life of old,*
> *may be found worthy to rise to the life of newborn children*
> *through water and the Holy Spirit.*

Take a moment to pray the first Luminous Mystery of the Rosary, Jesus' Baptism in the Jordan. Thank God for your own Baptism, at which your soul was imprinted with an indelible mark identifying you as God's own.

_____

_____

_____

_____

_____

_____

_____

_____

_____

_____

_____

_____

COMMIT–DAY 2
EUCHARIST

During the Mass in the first Eucharistic Prayer, after the bread and wine are changed into the Body, Blood, Soul, and Divinity of Christ, the priest prays,

Rome - fresco of Last Supper of Christ form church Santa Prassede © Renata Sedmakova / shutterstock.com

> *"Be pleased to look upon these offerings with a serene and kindly countenance, and to accept them, as once you were pleased to accept the gifts of your servant Abel the just, the sacrifice of Abraham, our father in faith, and the offering of your high priest Melchizedek, a holy sacrifice, a spotless victim."* —Eucharistic Prayer I

These words of the Church's liturgy remind us that God prepared for and prefigured this great sacrament in numerous ways in salvation history.

Look up the following verses. How do they prefigure the Eucharist?

Genesis 2:9; 3:22-24 _____

Genesis 4:4 _____

Genesis 14:18-20 _____

Genesis 22:1-14 _____

Exodus 12:17-24 _____

Exodus 16:4 _____

Jesus gives us food with everlasting benefits saying, "I am the living bread which came down from heaven; if any one eats of this bread, he will live forever; and the bread which I shall give for the life of the world is my flesh" (John 6:51). The disciples are astounded at this claim; many are offended and walk away, unwilling to believe the words of Christ.

The Apostles, however, do not depart from following Jesus, recognizing that he has the words of eternal life, and, as a result, are present at the Last Supper where Jesus promise and the prefigurements of the Old Testament are fulfilled. Jesus takes bread, saying, "This is my body which is given for you. Do this in remembrance of me" (Luke 22:19). Then, likewise with the chalice, "This cup which is poured out for you is the new covenant of my blood" (Luke 22:20). Jesus, the Lamb and beloved Son of God, changes the bread and wine into his Body and Blood, offering the perfect gift of himself in thanksgiving to the Father, and leaving us a new manna to sustain us on earth as we journey toward eternal life in the promised land of Heaven.

Jesus commissioned the Apostles to offer this communion in remembrance of him. We find the first written account of the fulfillment of this command in the narrative of Pentecost, just ten days after Christ's Ascension, when Acts describes that the first Christians "held steadfastly to the apostles' teaching and fellowship, to *the breaking of bread* and the prayers" (Acts 2:42, emphasis added).

This description assures us that the commemoration of Jesus' Last Supper Eucharist and his suffering, Death, and Resurrection was initiated right from the beginnings of the nascent Church. St. Paul, in his first letter to the Corinthians written circa A.D. 56, recounts the institution of the Eucharist and then warns against unworthy reception of the Body of Christ (1 Corinthians 11:23-30). Clearly, the Eucharist was such a central part of the Church's worship that from the earliest days the Apostles guarded the fidelity of the Eucharistic liturgy.

The *Catechism* explains that we "who have been raised to the dignity of the royal priesthood by Baptism and configured more deeply to Christ by Confirmation participate with the whole community in the Lord's own sacrifice by means of the Eucharist" (CCC 1322). Like the early Christians, we too are to hold steadfastly "to the breaking of bread and the prayers."

> *"Taking part in the eucharistic sacrifice, which is the fount and apex of the whole Christian life, they offer the Divine Victim to God, and offer themselves along with It….Strengthened in Holy Communion by the Body of Christ, they then manifest in a concrete way that unity of the people of God which is suitably signified and wondrously brought about by this most august sacrament."*
> —*Lumen Gentium*, 11

As Dr. Healy noted, the Eucharist is a profound bond of unity. By partaking in the Eucharist, we are united with Christ the head and with the whole Body of Christ, both on earth and in Heaven.

Take time to pray the fifth Luminous Mystery of the Rosary, the Institution of the Eucharist. Reflect on the truth that the Eucharist, which truly is the Body and Blood of Jesus, is "the source and summit of the Christian life" (CCC 1324).

COMMIT–DAY 3
PAUL AT TROAS

Preaching of Saint Paul / Scala / Art Resource, NY

After his Damascus Road conversion experience, Saul's zeal is redirected by the Holy Spirit toward building up, instead of persecuting, the nascent Church. Saul, now known by his Latin name Paul, undertakes several missionary journeys all around the eastern Mediterranean from Jerusalem and Samaria to Asia, Greece, and Macedonia, tirelessly preaching Jesus Christ to the inhabitants of those areas. During his third missionary journey, Paul visits Troas, a town near the coast of the Aegean Sea. And while in Troas he miraculously restores a young man to life.

LECTIO: The practice of praying with Scripture, *lectio divina*, begins with an active and close reading of the Scripture passage. Read the verse below and then answer the questions to take a closer look at some of the details of the passage.

> *"Sopater of Beroea, the son of Pyrrhus, accompanied him; and of the Thessalonians, Aristarchus and Secundus; and Gaius of Derbe, and Timothy; and the Asians, Tychicus and Trophimus. These went on and were waiting for us at Troas, but we sailed away from Philippi after the days of Unleavened Bread, and in five days we came to them at Troas, where we stayed for seven days. On the first day of the week, when we were gathered together to break bread, Paul talked with them, intending to depart on the morrow; and he prolonged his speech until midnight. There were many lights in the upper chamber where we were gathered. And a young man named Eutychus was sitting in the window. He sank into a deep sleep as Paul talked still longer; and being overcome by sleep, he fell down from the third story and was taken up dead. But Paul went down and bent over him, and embracing him said, 'Do not be alarmed, for his life is in him.' And when Paul had gone up and had broken bread and eaten, he conversed with them a long while, until daybreak, and so departed. And they took the lad away alive, and were not a little comforted."*
>
> —Acts 20:4-12

Although some of Scripture's details may appear extraneous to us, we can often learn much from them if we pay close attention. St. Luke provides some specific details about this gathering. How many men meet St. Paul in Troas? What are their names and where are they from?

_____

_____

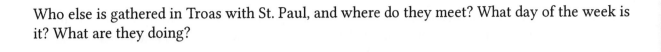

Who else is gathered in Troas with St. Paul, and where do they meet? What day of the week is it? What are they doing?

_____

_____

When Eutychus falls out the window and dies, St. Paul goes to him and restores him to life. How does he accomplish this, and what words does he use?

_____

_____

MEDITATIO: *Lectio*, a close reading and rereading, is followed by *meditatio*, time to reflect on the Scripture passage and to ponder the reason for particular events, descriptions, details, phrases, and even echoes from other Scripture passages that were noticed during *lectio*. Take some time now to meditate on the verse from page 108.

Imagine joining the gathering on the Lord's Day in an "upper chamber" with Sts. Paul, Luke, Timothy and others to "break bread," to celebrate the Eucharist. The main celebrant is Paul, who you have heard so much about and are anxious to hear preach. This is the same man who once persecuted the Church but after an amazing encounter with Jesus on the Road to Damascus has been transformed into a zealous and tireless evangelist. He has preached all over Asia, Macedonia, and Greece, drawing thousands of new believers into the Church. He has endured many hardships, including imprisonment, beating, and stoning. But he has survived it all and now he is here preaching. This will be your only opportunity to hear him as he plans to depart for Jerusalem in the morning. The Jewish celebration of Unleavened Bread has recently concluded, and you are anxious to hear what Paul will teach about the new Passover. It is getting quite late—it's almost midnight and there are "many lights in the upper chamber," yet Paul preaches on. You notice that Eutychus has fallen into a deep sleep. Suddenly, you look over but he is no longer sitting on the windowsill. All hearts stop at the sound of Eutychus' body hitting the ground, having fallen from a height of three stories. Everyone rushes to his side, but he is dead.

Calmly St. Paul lays his body on top of the youth and embraces him. The crowd looks on in wonder. Then Paul speaks: "Do not be alarmed, for his life is in him." You can hardly believe your eyes as you witness Eutychus take in a breath. You are reminded of Elijah raising the son of the widow in Zarephath (1 Kings 17:19-23) and of Jesus raising Lazarus (John 11:1-44). What is this power? What is this life that is in Eutychus, raised on this Lord's Day, the day of Christ's Resurrection? You approach the Eucharist with a new awe at the life you are about to receive in this breaking of the bread.

Numerous believers from various locations meet St. Paul in Troas. Recalling his words in Galatians 3:28 that "you all are one in Christ Jesus," how does this story witness to the fellowship among believers in the early Church?

_____

_____

_____

This *lectio* Scripture passage gives us another account of the early Christians meeting on the Lord's Day to pray and break bread as was first described in Acts 2:42. How does the description of the activities in the Upper Room at Troas reflect the Eucharistic liturgy? What else was celebrated in an "upper room?" What does all this tell us about the importance of attending Mass particularly on Sunday, the Lord's Day?

_____

_____

_____

After St. Paul revives Eutychus, he proceeds with the breaking of the bread. What effect do you think receiving the Eucharist has on Eutychus after his death-to-life experience? What should the reception of Holy Communion affect in us?

_____

_____

_____

ORATIO, CONTEMPLATIO, RESOLUTIO: Having read and meditated on today's Scripture passage, take some time to bring your thoughts to God (*oratio*) and engage God in silence (*contemplatio*). Then end your prayer by making a simple concrete resolution (*resolutio*) to respond to God's prompting of your heart in today's prayer.

_____

_____

_____

The *Catechism* affirms that there are three "sacraments of Christian initiation," Baptism, Eucharist, and Confirmation, "whose unity must be safeguarded" (CCC 1285). Together these sacraments lay the foundation for the Christian life. The Sacrament of Confirmation strengthens and completes baptismal grace and prepares us to evangelize and defend the faith.

Confirmation, like all the sacraments, has its roots in the salvation history of the Old Testament. The two key gestures, imposition of hands and anointing with oil, have rich symbolism in the Old Testament. They are the traditional Jewish means of asking for God's blessing and for setting a person, or thing, apart for a special task.

The window of a cathedral of St. Peter in Vatican, with a dove representing the Holy Spirit
© Dan Costa / shutterstock.com

Priestly Blessing / © Balage Balogh / Art Resource, NY

In the Old Testament, we see the imposition of hands used in two ways. The first is for blessing. In Genesis 48:13-14, Jacob blesses Joseph's sons by laying his hands on their heads while invoking a prayer of blessing. In Leviticus 9:22, the Levitical priest raises his hands over the people to bless them. However, the primary way that imposition of hands is used in the Old Testament is to set apart for a special task.

Look up Numbers 27:18-23. Who receives the imposition of hands and for what purpose?

_____

_____

The second gesture used in Confirmation, anointing with oil, also finds its origins in the Old Testament, where anointing is used to set apart leaders for three types of ministries: priest, prophet, and king. Look up the following verses and describe who is being anointed and for what purpose. What do these Scripture verses specifically tell us happens to those who are anointed prophets or kings?

Exodus 28:40-41 _____

1 Samuel 9:27-10:1; 10:6 _____

1 Samuel 16:1-13 _____

1 Kings 19:16 _____

2 Kings 2:9-15 _____

111

The Hebrew word for the verb "to anoint" is *mashach*, the root for the title Messiah, which means Anointed One. God promises through the prophets, particularly Isaiah, that he will send a Servant of the Lord, a son of David, who will establish his kingdom forever and save his people. The Spirit of the Lord will be upon him because he is the Anointed One (Isaiah 61:1). The descent of the Spirit upon Jesus at his Baptism in the Jordan is the sign that he is the promised Messiah. Jesus makes this claim himself in the Nazareth synagogue (Luke 4:16-21) by reading the prophet Isaiah and announcing that he is the fulfillment of this prophecy.

This gift of the Spirit is meant to be communicated to all the people gathered into God's family. Jesus promises an outpouring of the Spirit on numerous occasions. The promise is first fulfilled on the night of the Resurrection when the risen Lord appears to his disciples in the Upper Room behind closed doors and breathes on them so they receive the Holy Spirit (John 20:19-23). Then, on Pentecost, the Holy Spirit falls upon the disciples in a mighty and public way, and they are transformed into persuasive evangelists and faithful disciples. They immediately go out and begin to proclaim the risen Christ (Acts 2). Many people are moved to conversion and are baptized. After this experience, the Apostles begin to travel out from Jerusalem to fulfill Christ's command to go make disciples of all nations.

These Old Testament actions point forward to the anointing with chrism oil and laying on of hands while invoking a blessing used in the Sacrament of Confirmation. In the Roman Rite, the bishop extends his hands in a gesture that signifies the Holy Spirit as he invokes a blessing of the outpouring of the Holy Spirit on the confirmands:

> *"All-powerful God, Father of our Lord Jesus Christ,*
> *by water and the Holy Spirit*
> *you freed your sons and daughters from sin*
> *and gave them new life.*
> *Send your Holy Spirit upon them to be their helper and guide.*
> *Give them the spirit of wisdom and understanding,*
> *the spirit of right judgment and courage,*
> *the spirit of knowledge and reverence.*
> *Fill them with the spirit of wonder and awe in your presence.*
> *We ask this through Christ our Lord."*   —CCC 1299

Then "the sacrament of Confirmation is conferred through the anointing with chrism on the forehead, which is done by the laying on of the hand, and through the words: ...'Be sealed with the Gift of the Holy Spirit'" (CCC 1300). The rite concludes with the sign of peace signifying the ecclesial communion with the bishop and the faithful. The confirmed are now equipped, called, and set apart for the mission of the Church, to bear witness to our crucified and risen Lord, Jesus Christ.

Take time to pray the third Glorious Mystery of the Rosary, the Descent of the Holy Spirit at Pentecost. Ask God to renew in you "the spirit of wisdom and understanding, the spirit of right judgment and courage, the spirit of knowledge and reverence" and to fill you anew "with the spirit of wonder and awe" in God's presence.

COMMIT—DAY 5
TRUTH AND BEAUTY

***Moses Striking the Rock**, Jacopo Tintoretto, c. 1577,
Scuola Grande di San Rocco, Venice, Italy*

Moses striking the rock / Cameraphoto Arte, Venice / Art Resource, NY

This painting is found in the Scuola Grande di San Rocco in Venice, Italy. The Scuola was not a school but a confraternity. During the Middle Ages and Renaissance, a confraternity was an association of lay people who banded together to perform works of charity. This confraternity was founded in the sixteenth century to help the poor, particularly the sick during epidemics or plague—the protector saint against the plague, St. Rocco, was their patron. It was a center for charity and aid to the poor, but also a place of prayer and devotion.

In the sixteenth century, Jacopo Tintoretto was commissioned by the confraternity to decorate the walls and ceilings of the Scuola. He began this lifelong project just after the end of the last session of the Council of Trent, at which time the Church encouraged works of art that led to deeper devotion and understanding of the faith. This series of paintings is rich in theological insight. One of the first paintings that he finished for the Scuola was the enormous *Crucifixion*. The other thirty-seven paintings completed by Tintoretto are to be interpreted in light of the Cross, thus illustrating that the Cross is the origin of salvation and the grace received in the sacraments.

This work depicts the dramatic miracle of Moses striking the rock as God's people make their way to Mount Sinai (Exodus 17:1-7). The Chosen People cry out for water as they make their way across a parched and arid land. God tells Moses to take the same rod with which he performed signs and wonders in Egypt and with which he parted the Red Sea and strike the rock. Moses did as God commanded, and Tintoretto captures the very moment that water rushes out from the rock.

Crucifixion / Alfredo Dagli Orti / Art Resource, NY

Observe the water flowing from the rock in the upper portion of the scene. This water is usually depicted as a fountain in art, yet Tintoretto elects to show the water gushing forth in a spurt from the rock. This is by design on the part of Tintoretto; he intends it to resemble paintings of the crucifixion, which portray blood and water flowing out of the side of Christ and angels catching the blood and water in containers. Tintoretto reproduces with paint that ancient typological interpretation that the miracle of water from the rock prefigures the blood and water flowing from the side of Christ. This water, the Church tells us, which flowed from Christ's side represents Baptism; the blood which flowed signifies the Eucharist. These two foundational sacraments for the Christian find their origin in Christ's redeeming sacrifice on the Cross.

"The blood and water that flowed from the pierced side of the crucified Jesus are types of Baptism and the Eucharist, the sacraments of new life. From then on, it is possible 'to be born of water and the Spirit' in order to enter the Kingdom of God."

—CCC 1225

Typology: *"The Church, as early as apostolic times, and then constantly in her Tradition, has illuminated the unity of the divine plan in the Old and New Testaments through typology, which discerns in God's works of the Old Covenant prefigurations of what he accomplished in the fullness of time in the person of his incarnate Son."*   —CCC 128

Tintoretto underscores the relation of Baptism and the scene from Exodus by depicting Moses in the same garb and pose as Christ in the other paintings in the Scuola di San Rocco. Moreover, the painter fashions Moses's rod into a cross, further solidifying this interpretation. The theological meaning of the painting becomes clear: Jesus Christ, the New Moses, quenches the thirst of all mankind by his Passion and Death. Christ is the fountain of the Spirit that truly quenches our thirst. He truly is the "living water" (John 4:10-15; 7:37-38). The water from the rock is a foreshadowing of the grace of the Holy Spirit that is poured into our hearts and the new life in Christ we receive at Baptism.

Tintoretto did not invent the symbolic connection between Jesus and the rock in the wilderness; it was an association made by St. Paul himself. Read 1 Corinthians 10:1-4. How is the rock from which the Israelites drank water a foreshadowing of Christ?

_____

_____

_____

Note how the painting abounds with life. Tintoretto creates intense dynamism in this painting: God the Father, the dynamic act and power behind the miracle, on the right atop a dark cloud; the Israelites below frantically capturing the water that pours forth from the rock into various containers in a semi-circular group of movement. This motion of the Israelites and God the Father gives the impression of rotating movement, contrasted with Moses, who, along with the rock, is solid and immovable. Even the interplay between light and darkness affects a feeling of rhythm and movement. This sense of action draws the viewer up into the drama of the scene, inviting him to be part of the event itself.

Imagine you had been struck by the plague in sixteenth-century Venice and were taken in by the Confraternity of St. Rocco. As you lay in bed recovering in the large upstairs hall, you open your eyes to behold this incredible scene painted across the ceiling. Just as God quenched the thirst of the Israelites through Moses, you had received not only water, but food and medical care from the lay people in the confraternity. The goodness of these Christian men and women causes you to reconsider that Christ is the living water, given so that you might never thirst again, and that he is the Divine Physician, who wants to heal all your sins. Lying there you contemplate the intermingling of the story of salvation and your own life.

May we be those lay men and women in our world whose words and actions, like this beautiful painting, direct many to Christ.

Take a moment to journal your ideas, questions, or insights about this lesson. Write down thoughts you had that may not have been mentioned in the text or the discussion questions. List any personal applications you got from the lessons. What challenged you the most in the teachings? How might you turn what you've learned into specific action?

_____

_____

_____

_____

_____

_____

_____

_____

_____

_____

_____

_____

_____

_____

_____

_____

_____

_____

_____

SESSION 7

LEADERSHIP IN THE CHURCH

OPENING PRAYER

Come Holy Spirit,
fill the hearts of your faithful
and enkindle in them the fire of your love.
Send forth your Spirit
and they shall be created.
And you shall renew the face of the earth.

Let us pray.
O, God, who did instruct the hearts of the faithful
by the light of the Holy Spirit,
grant that by the same Holy Spirit
we may be truly wise
and ever rejoice in his consolation.
Through Christ our Lord.
Amen.

Sts. Timothy and Titus, pray for us.

INTRODUCTION

The Holy Spirit empowered Jesus' disciples to spread the gospel message. As the number of believers increased, the need for effective leadership grew. One of the keys to the early Church's growth and unity was the leadership structure that Christ established when he chose and formed the twelve Apostles and gave St. Peter the keys of the kingdom (Matthew 16:18-19). The foundations for the Church's ordained positions such as bishops, priests, and deacons are already present in the Acts of the Apostles and the New Testament. Here we also see these roles in action as the early Church cares for the believers and discerns its first doctrinal questions and sends out pastoral direction.

Shining dove with rays on a blue background © Molodec / shutterstock.com

CONNECT

Think of an experience, whether in a personal or professional capacity, where you were part of a team of people trying to come a decision. What was that like? If you've been in that situation more than once, feel free to compare and contrast events—did certain conditions make one circumstance more productive or successful than another? Please share.

Now think about a situation where you worked with a partner, whether at a job or on a particular project. How did you support each other? In what ways did working together help you do a better job?

DISCUSS

PART 1: APOSTLES, ELDERS, AND DEACONS
Watch the teaching on video. The following is a brief outline of the topics covered.

I. Three Specific Roles in Church Leadership
  A. Apostles
    1. Highest role
    2. Church led by Spirit, but under
       blessing/supervision of the Apostles
    3. Primary role is teaching/preaching
    4. Apex of teaching role to lead believers
       in celebration of sacraments

  B. Deacons (Acts 6)
    1. Hellenist widows being neglected
       (Hellenists: Jews who speak Greek; Jews:
       Jews who speak Hebrew/Aramaic)

  2. Need leaders to serve under Apostles;
     natural gifts and filled with Holy Spirit   _____
  3. Collegial decision
  4. Apostles confer authority by laying   _____
     on of hands   _____
  5. Role of deacon is to serve   _____
  C. Elders (Acts 14:23; Acts 20:24-32)
     1. Leaders of local Church   _____
     2. Must do what St. Paul has done   _____
     3. Guardians/shepherds of the flock   _____
     4. God equips those who are called   _____

II. What This Means for Us Today   _____
    A. Three hierarchy roles develop—Bishop,   _____
       Elders (Priests), Deacons
       1. Bishop, Greek *episkopos,* overseer   _____
       2. Priests (elders), Greek *presbyteros,* elder _____
       3. Deacon, Greek *diakonos,* minister/servant   _____
    B. Corresponds to Old Testament High Priest,
       Priests, Levites   _____

DISCUSS

1. What was the primary role of the Apostles? Think of a bishop or priest who is a good preacher/teacher. What is it about his preaching/teaching that you like?

_____

_____

2. Why were deacons needed in the Church and what role did they play when commissioned? What roles do deacons serve in the Church today?

_____

_____

3. What three-fold hierarchy in the Old Testament corresponds to the leadership structure in the Church?

_____

_____

PART 2: COUNCIL OF JERUSALEM
Watch the video teaching. The following is a brief outline of the topics covered.

I. How Are Decisions Made? (Acts 15)
  A. Question of circumcision
  B. Local church looks to mother Church for
    doctrinal authority
  C. Church gathers together, collegiality; debate
  D. St. Peter, head of the Apostles, speaks authoritatively
  E. Then St. James, bishop of the Jerusalem
    church, speaks
     1. Gives direction on pastoral implementation
     2. Gentiles obligated by moral law, but not
       Torah ritual laws
     3. Abstain from cultural expressions
       of idolatry
     4. Put off practices of their old life
  F. The Church is universal/catholic

II. A Model for Decision-Making
  A. Delegation and letter sent with decision
  B. Decision of "the Holy Spirit and...us"
  C. Exercise of magisterium of Church

DISCUSS

4. What issue was resolved during the Council of Jerusalem?

_____

_____

5. After all opinions were heard, who rose and spoke doctrinally to the Church? Once Church doctrine was defined, someone else spoke. Who was that and why did he have the authority to speak?

_____

_____

6. What were the basic practices from which Gentiles were asked to abstain? Why were these practices prohibited? How are all Christians called to put away the practices of their old life?

_____

_____

PART 3: CO-WORKERS IN CHRIST
Watch the video teaching. The following is a brief outline of the topics covered.

I. Collaboration
    A. Jesus sends disciples out in pairs
    B. St. Paul follows Jesus' instruction;   _____
       (nearly 100 names associated with St. Paul   _____
       in New Testament)
    C. St. Paul practices servant leadership   _____
    D. St. Paul works with and mentors people   _____
       (i.e., Timothy, Luke, Aquila, and Priscilla, etc.)   _____

II. How Did St. Paul Train Others?   _____
    A. Brought them with him so they could watch him   _____
    B. Then he watched them as they began to work   _____

III. Laity in the Church Today   _____
     A. "Exercise their apostolate in the world"   _____
        (*Decree on the Apostolate of the Laity*, 2)
     B. Laypeople imbue all areas of their life   _____
        with the spirit of the gospel
     C. Indispensable role in Church's mission   _____
     D. How the Church build up
        1. "...to equip the saints for the work of   _____
           ministry, for building up the body of
           Christ" (Ephesians 4:11-12)   _____
        2. Leadership is to equip laity to be sent out   _____
     E. Parish not about maintenance, but about mission _____

DISCUSS

7. Why did Jesus send his disciples out two by two? How does St. Paul follow this instruction of Jesus?

_____

_____

8. Take a closer look at the section of Vatican II's *Apostolicam Actuositatem (Decree on the Apostolate of the Laity)* that Dr. Healy quoted:

> *"[The laity] exercise the apostolate in fact by their activity directed to the evangelization and sanctification of men and to the penetrating and perfecting of the temporal order through the spirit of the Gospel. In this way, their temporal activity openly bears witness to Christ and promotes the salvation of men. Since the laity, in accordance with their state of life, live in the midst of the world and its concerns, they are called by God to exercise their apostolate in the world like leaven, with the ardor of the spirit of Christ."*
> —*Apostolicam Actuositatem*, 2

What strikes you about this quote? How do you live this out in your own life?

_____

_____

_____

MEMORY VERSE

But thanks be to God, who in Christ always leads us in triumph, and through us spreads the fragrance of the knowledge of him everywhere."   —2 Corinthians 2:14

CLOSING PRAYER

"But you are a chosen race, a royal priesthood, a holy nation, God's own people, that you may declare the wonderful deeds of him who called you out of darkness into his marvelous light."
                                                            —1 Peter 2:9

Dear Lord,
every person on this earth
is called to proclaim your name.
Within your Church,
you have given each of us a particular calling.
Please Give us the courage and perseverance
to answer that call.
Help us to know you,
to love you and to serve you in this world,
to share your light with all those around us
and to glorify you in all things
until we stand before you on the last day.
Amen.

Sts. Timothy and Titus, pray for us.

FURTHER READING

Catechism of the Catholic Church, 901-913, "Priest, Prophet and King"

Catechism of the Catholic Church, 1536-1600, "The Sacrament of Holy Orders"

Pope St. John Paul II: Apostolic Exhortation *Christifideles Laici (On the Vocation and the Mission of the Lay Faithful in the Church and in the World)*

Rev. Robert Barron, *"Seeds of the Word: Finding God in the Culture"*

COMMIT—DAY 1
APOSTLES AND PRIESTS

After stating that "every one who calls upon the name of the Lord will be saved" (Romans 10:13), St. Paul goes on to ask, "But how are men to call upon [Jesus] in whom they have not believed? And how are they to believe in him of whom they have never heard? And how are they to hear without a preacher?" (Romans 10:14). Paul is clear: "Faith comes from what is heard, and what is heard comes by the preaching of Christ" (Romans 10:17).

Paul Preaches to the Thessalonians, drawings by Gustave Dore © Nicku / shutterstock.com

Jesus gives the Apostles a particular role, mission, and authority, and at the heart of that mission is "the preaching of Christ." We see this truth from the very beginning of Jesus' own ministry. After his temptation in the desert, Jesus returns to Galilee and begins his preaching ministry in Capernaum, "Repent, for the kingdom of heaven is at hand" (Matthew 4:17). Read Matthew 4:17-22. What are Jesus' next recorded words?

_____

_____

After the Apostles have been with Jesus for some time, Jesus sends them out two by two. Read Matthew 10:1-7. What does Jesus send them out to do?

_____

Read Matthew 28:19-20. Just before his Ascension into heaven, what mission does Jesus give to the Apostles?

_____

Jesus chose and formed twelve Apostles, knowing the mission for which he was preparing them. With Jesus' Ascension back to the Father, it was Jesus' Apostles who would acknowledge Jesus Christ before men (Matthew 10:32) in their preaching, teaching, and exercise of the sacraments. This is exactly what we see in Acts of the Apostles as St. Peter preaches at Pentecost, at the Temple gate, before the high priest, rulers, scribes, and council, to Cornelius and his household, etc. and then baptizing those who come to faith; and as St. Paul preaches in city after city throughout Asia minor, Macedonia, and Greece. This apostolic focus on preaching and teaching "Jesus Christ crucified" is why additional men are chosen and ordained deacons—so that the Apostles can devote themselves "to prayer and to the ministry of the word" (Acts 6:4). As the *Catechism of the Catholic Church* says: "Bishops, with priests as co-workers, have as their first task 'to preach the Gospel of God to all men' in keeping with the Lord's command" (CCC 888).

Just as Jesus spoke only what his Father in Heaven commanded, so too the Apostles teach and preach what they witnessed and what Jesus and the Spirit command and direct. Thus St. Paul can say, "For I received from the Lord what I also delivered to you" (1 Corinthians 11:23). St. John closes his gospel stating that he is "bearing witness to these things" (John 21:24) and writes in his first letter that "that which we have seen and heard we proclaim also to you" (1 John 1:3). St. Peter too describes himself "as a fellow elder and a witness of the sufferings of Christ" (1 Peter 5:1).

Read 1 Corinthians 11:1-2 and 2 Thessalonians 2:15. Having received the apostolic preaching, what does the Apostle Paul exhort us to do? In what two ways is this teaching given to us? And by whom?

_____

_____

The Apostles understood that their role was not to end with the death of the twelve men chosen by Jesus at the beginning of his ministry, but, rather, it was to be handed on to others. Thus St. Peter, speaking of the absence left after Judas Iscariot's betrayal and death says, "His office let another take" (Acts 1:20), and the Apostles choose St. Matthias to replace Judas (Acts 1:15-26). The Apostles also understand that they are to hand down the faith and traditions to the next generation. Sts. Timothy and Titus are examples of faithful young men who are ordained priests by St. Paul and become bishops of Ephesus and Crete, respectively.

St. Paul writes two letters to St. Timothy. Read 1 Timothy 4:6-16 and 2 Timothy 4:2. According to Paul, what are bishops to attend to?

_____

St. Paul praises those priests/elders "who labor in preaching and teaching" (1 Timothy 5:17), and St. James reminds the faithful to call for the elders to administer the sacraments (James 5:14-15). Paul will exhort St. Timothy, as a bishop (*episkopos*), that what he has heard "from me [Paul] before many witnesses entrust to faithful men who will be able to teach others also" (2 Timothy 2:2); thus the first Apostles entrust the deposit of the faith to a new generation, and so on until the present day, and until the day when Jesus will come again.

It took some time for the offices that we recognize today to take concrete shape. But already by the end of the first century, the terms bishop, priest, and deacon are in common use, as is evident in the writings of St. Ignatius of Antioch from the year 110 A.D.:

St. Ignatius of Antioch holding a letter / © DeA Picture Library / Art Resource, NY

"Now, therefore, it has been my privilege to see you in the person of your God-inspired bishop, Damas; and in the persons of your worthy presbyters, Bassus and Apollonius; and my fellow-servant, the deacon, Zotion. What a delight is his company! For he is subject to the bishop as to the grace of God, and to the presbytery as to the law of Jesus Christ."
—St. Ignatius of Antioch, *Letter to the Magnesians*, 2 [A.D. 110]

It is clear, not only that Christ intended for the Apostles to lead his Church, with St. Peter at the helm, but also that he intended that they be succeeded by others, who would further his kingdom until the end of time. The Apostles "filled Jerusalem with [their] teaching" (Acts 5:28), and their successors, the bishops and priests whom we look to as shepherds today, are those called to that same mission of filling the world with the preaching of Jesus Christ.

Take some time today to meditate on the gift of Holy Mother Church. In what ways does her leadership directly affect your life? How would your life be different if you didn't have her? How is it better because you do? Offer a prayer of intercession for the direction of the Holy Spirit upon the Church, the Holy Father, and all priests. Offer a prayer of thanksgiving for the wisdom and great generosity of our Father in heaven, for his constant care, and for the loving hand with which he continues to guide his children.

St. Peter at Assumption Cathedral, Thailand © thaagoon / shutterstock.com

COMMIT–DAY 2
DEACONS AND SERVING THE POOR

Saint Stephen Consecrated Deacon / Restored Tradition Art

The word *deacon* comes from the Greek word *diakonos*, which means *minister* or *servant*. Through our Baptism and Confirmation, each of us is called to be a servant of Christ, but some are called to be a public sign to the world of the servant leadership of Christ through sacramental ordination to the diaconate.

The first deacons are ordained by the Apostles to address some practical needs in the early Church.

Read Acts 6:1-6. As the numbers of believers increased, some complaints were raised. Who issued the complaint, and why? What did the Apostles do about it?

_____

_____

To what did the Twelve declare that they would remain devoted?

_____

_____

Whom did the assembly choose as the first deacons?

_____

_____

Once they were selected, how were they ordained?

_____

_____

Read Acts 8:4-5, 12. In addition to serving the material needs of the faithful, what else did the ministry of deacons include in the early Church?

_____

_____

Through the centuries, different aspects of the diaconate have been emphasized. By the fourth century, the diaconate had gradually become a step in the process of becoming a priest. As such, it came to be considered a "transitional" office. But in the 1960s, Pope St. Paul VI formally reclaimed the office of deacon within the Catholic Church to be a permanent order of ministry. Thus in addition to "transitional deacons" (those men who are ordained deacons for a period of time ahead of their priestly ordination), the Church also ordains men as "permanent deacons" (those men who are ordained deacons but not pursuing priestly ordination).

As a member of the clergy, a deacon shares in the Sacrament of Orders. Unlike bishops and priests, with whom they share in the sacrament, deacons also have one foot planted squarely in community life—many are married with families and often hold a full-time job outside of ministry.

Because of a deacon's close proximity to the world through his family and his work, he is in a unique position to bring Christ's presence to the world. By faithfully carrying out the corporal works of mercy within his community, a deacon has the ability to extend the doors of the local church out into the world, stretching the merciful hands of Christ to the farthest corners of his community.

Read 1 Timothy 3:8-13. At the end of the passage, St. Paul explains why deacons must meet the requirements listed. What reasons does he give?

_____

_____

From the very beginning, the Church was careful to appoint only the most respected and faithful of believers. Is there a deacon assigned to your local parish? If so, think about all the ways in which he serves your parish. If you don't know how he is involved, ask around. You might be amazed at how many ministries have your deacon listed as the contact person. At your earliest opportunity, go out of your way to thank your deacon for all he does, and offer to assist him in the service of your parish where you can. Let us pray for our deacons, that they may continue to serve their communities with great love and mercy, proclaiming Christ to the world in all they say and do.

Holy God, Saint Vincent served You as a permanent deacon and gave his whole life and soul to You, even to the point of becoming a martyr. I lift up to You the deacons of the Church and all those who are being called by God to become deacons. Guide them as they discern how to serve the Body of Christ. Prevent the attractions of the world and the busyness of secular jobs from interfering with their vocations. Teach them to grow in humility. Help their families learn from their examples and support their diaconates with trust and joy. Saint Vincent, pray for us. Amen.
—St. Vincent's Prayer for Deacons

St. Vincent, deacon, martyr / Album / Art Resource, NY

COMMIT–DAY 3
COUNCIL OF JERUSALEM

As Cornelius the centurion, the Ethiopian eunuch, and other Gentiles accept the Gospel and become baptized believers, a doctrinal controversy arises over whether Gentiles will be subject to the entire Mosaic Law. The early Church gathers in Jerusalem to address the growing concern, and the interaction of the Apostles and elders highlights the Holy Spirit's leading of God's people through the Church Christ establishes on St. Peter and the Apostles.

> **LECTIO:** The practice of praying with Scripture, *lectio divina*, begins with an active and close reading of the Scripture passage. Read the Scripture passage below and then answer the questions to take a closer look at some of the details of the passage.

"When they came to Jerusalem, they were welcomed by the church and the apostles and the elders, and they declared all that God had done with them. But some believers who belonged to the party of the Pharisees rose up, and said, 'It is necessary to circumcise them, and to charge them to keep the law of Moses.' The apostles and the elders were gathered together to consider this matter. And after there had been much debate, Peter rose and said to them, 'Brethren, you know that in the early days God made choice among you, that by my mouth the Gentiles should hear the word of the gospel and believe. And God who knows the heart bore witness to them, giving them the Holy Spirit just as he did to us; and he made no distinction between us and them, but cleansed their hearts by faith. Now therefore why do you make trial of God by putting a yoke upon the neck of the disciples which neither our fathers nor we have been able to bear? But we believe that we shall be saved through the grace of the Lord Jesus, just as they will.' And all the assembly kept silence; and they listened to Barnabas and Paul as they related what signs and wonders God had done through them among the Gentiles."

—Acts 15:4-12

Who stood in favor of requiring the Gentiles to adhere to the Law of Moses, including circumcision?

_____

_____

Who met together to discuss the issue and make a determination?

_____

After "much debate," who stood up and spoke, and what did he say?

_____

_____

What did the assembly do when St. Peter finished speaking? What does this tell us about his role among the leaders in the Church?

_____

_____

MEDITATIO: *Lectio*, a close reading and rereading, is followed by *meditatio*, time to reflect on the Scripture passage and to ponder the reason for particular events, descriptions, details, phrases, and even echoes from other Scripture passages that were noticed during *lectio*. Take some time now to meditate on the Scripture passage from page 128.

The following mediation is taken from Pope St. John Paul II's encyclical *Redemptoris Missio (Mission of the Redeemer)*.

> *"The Holy Spirit is indeed the principal agent of the whole of the Church's mission. His action is preeminent in the mission ad gentes [to the nations], as can clearly be seen in the early Church: in the conversion of Cornelius (cf. Acts 10), in the decisions made about emerging problems (cf. Acts 15) and in the choice of regions and peoples to be evangelized (cf. Acts 16:6ff). The Spirit worked through the apostles, but at the same time he was also at work in those who heard them,...Paul and Barnabas are impelled by the Spirit to go to the Gentiles (cf. Acts 13:46-48), a development not without certain tensions and problems. How are these converted Gentiles to live their faith in Jesus? Are they bound by the traditions of Judaism and the law of circumcision? At the first Council, which gathers the members of the different churches together with the apostles in Jerusalem, a decision is taken which is acknowledged as coming from the Spirit: it is not necessary for a Gentile to submit to the Jewish Law in order to become a Christian (cf. Acts 15:5-11, 28). From now on the Church opens her doors and becomes the house which all may enter, and in which all can feel at home, while keeping their own culture and traditions, provided that these are not contrary to the Gospel."*
> —Pope St. John Paul II, *Redemptoris Missio*, 21, 24

Having made their decision, the Apostles and elders send Paul, Barnabas, Judas, and Silas to Antioch with a letter articulating the council's decision. Even though our *lectio* passage primarily describes the Apostles and elders debating and speaking, the Church's letter is clear that the decision comes not simply from men, but from "the Holy Spirit and...us" (Acts 15:28). How do Jesus' words to the Apostles in John 16:13 help us understand this description?

_____

_____

Read Galatians 3. In his letter to the Galatians, likely written before the Council of Jerusalem, St. Paul (a zealous Jewish Pharisee himself before his Damascus Road conversion) reminds his readers that Abraham was righteous by faith, not by the Mosaic Law, which was given centuries after Abraham's death. He goes on to explain that the Law was given "because of transgressions" and was "our custodian until Christ came, that we might be justified by faith. But now that faith has come, we are no longer under a custodian" (Galatians 3:19, 24-25). God's Providence brings Paul, a young preeminent student of the Jewish teacher St. Gamaliel, to faith. With his incredible knowledge of the Scriptures, St. Paul will not only preach and evangelize, but also clearly articulate and explain why the Holy Spirit makes no distinction between Jew and Gentile. How does this show God's Providence in the early Church? How does Providence continue to lead the Church today? How has Providence worked in your own life?

_____

_____

_____

St. Augustine once wrote, "I would not believe the gospel if the authority of the Catholic Church did not move me to do so." How do St. Augustine's words reinforce the importance of looking to the Church for doctrinal truth?

_____

_____

_____

> **ORATIO, CONTEMPLATIO, RESOLUTIO:** Having read and meditated on today's Scripture passage, take some time to bring your thoughts to God (*oratio*) and engage God in silence (*contemplatio*). Then end your prayer by making a simple concrete resolution (*resolutio*) to respond to God's prompting of your heart in today's prayer.

Council of Trent old illustration / marzolino / shutterstock.com

COMMIT–DAY 4
CO-WORKERS: PARTNERS IN THE GOSPEL

Early in his pontificate, Pope St. John Paul II wrote *Christifideles Laici (On the Vocation and the Mission of the Lay Faithful in the Church and in the World)*. In this apostolic exhortation, he shares a vision for the laity that is empowering and energizing. Let's explore just a few passages from this document, and perhaps revitalize our perspective on the invaluable contribution that each of us is called to in fulfilling the mission of Christ.

> *"The lay members of Christ's Faithful people (Christifideles Laici)...are those who form that part of the People of God which might be likened to the labourers in the vineyard mentioned in Matthew's Gospel: 'For the Kingdom of heaven is like a householder who went out early in the morning to hire labourers for his vineyard. After agreeing with the labourers for a denarius a day, he sent them into his vineyard' (Matthew 20:1-2). The gospel parable sets before our eyes the Lord's vast vineyard and the multitude of persons, both women and men, who are called and sent forth by him to labour in it. The vineyard is the whole world (cf. Mt 13:38), which is to be transformed according to the plan of God in view of the final coming of the Kingdom of God."*
>
> —*Christifideles Laici, 1*

To whom does Pope St. John Paul II liken the laity?

_____

_____

What is the vineyard? And what are the laborers to do to it?

_____

_____

Further on, we read...

> *"We continue in our reading of the gospel parable: 'And about the eleventh hour he went out and found others standing; and he said to them, "Why do you stand here idle all day?" They said to him, "Because no one has hired us." He said to them, "You go into the vineyard too"' (Mt 20:6-7). Since the work that awaits everyone in the vineyard of the Lord is so great there is no place for idleness. With even greater urgency the 'householder' repeats his invitation: 'You go into my vineyard too.'"* —*Christifideles Laici, 3*

Read Romans 12:4-11. Think about your daily life. When it comes to working in the vineyard, have you been idle? How do you feel called to minister to the world? What are some things you can do in your daily life to fulfill that calling?

_____

_____

_____

"The 'world' thus becomes the place and the means for the lay faithful to fulfill their Christian vocation, because the world itself is destined to glorify God the Father in Christ. The Council is able then to indicate the proper and special sense of the divine vocation which is directed to the lay faithful. They are not called to abandon the position that they have in the world. Baptism does not take them from the world at all, as the apostle Paul points out: 'So, brethren, in whatever state each was called, there let him remain with God' (1 Corinthians 7:24). On the contrary, he entrusts a vocation to them that properly concerns their situation in the world. The lay faithful, in fact, 'are called by God so that they, led by the spirit of the Gospel, might contribute to the sanctification of the world, as from within like leaven, by fulfilling their own particular duties. Thus, especially in this way of life, resplendent in faith, hope and charity they manifest Christ to others.' Thus for the lay faithful, to be present and active in the world is not only an anthropological and sociological reality, but in a specific way, a theological and ecclesiological reality as well. In fact, in their situation in the world God manifests his plan and communicates to them their particular vocation of 'seeking the Kingdom of God by engaging in temporal affairs and by ordering them according to the plan of God.'" —Christifideles Laici, 15

It is often difficult to be a Christian in today's world, which seemingly becomes more and more secular by the day. But Christ knew this, and tells his disciples: "You will be hated by all for my name's sake" (Matthew 10:22). Pope St. John Paul II provides encouragement in the above passage, calling upon us not to remove ourselves from the world, but to extend Christ's light to the world.

As lay faithful, we are Christ's hands and feet in the world. We are laborers in the vineyard. We are commissioned to share Christ with the world. Lord, help us to squelch our propensity for idleness. Help us to go out into the vineyard, full of eagerness and joy, spreading the Gospel to all whom we meet, in both word and deed. Amen.

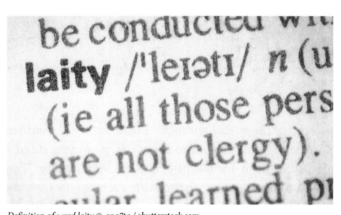

Definition of word laity © aga7ta / shutterstock.com

"Christianity is not a set of private convictions that we cultivate inwardly or whisper among ourselves. It is the message that the whole world needs to hear. We who have heard it must become agents of subversion and transformation."
—Bishop Robert E. Barron, *Exploring Catholic Theology: Essays on God, Liturgy, and Evangelization*

Saint Peter Ordaining the First Deacons,
11th–12th century, Tokali Kilise, Goreme, Cappadocia

Saint Peter Ordaining the First Deacons / Gianni Dagli Orti / the Art Archive at Art Resource, NY

This beautiful and remarkably well-preserved fresco can be seen in the Church of Tokali Kilise in Cappadocia, Turkey, the region from which hailed the Cappadocian fathers: St. Basil the Great, St. Gregory Nazianzus, and Gregory of Nyssa. This part of Cappadocia is known for its unique rock formations, the result of volcanic activity in ancient times. The ash hardens to a soft rock, which can easily be carved into homes and buildings. The area abounds with countless churches, chapels, and monastic structures all carved from this soft rock.

Saint Peter Ordaining the First Deacons recalls the selection of seven men of good character, full of the Holy Spirit and wisdom, who are ordained deacons by the Apostles to assist with the distribution of food so that the Apostles can focus on "preaching the Word of God" (Acts 6:1-6).

The deacon's primary role of service is depicted in their clothing. If we look closely at the detail of one of the deacons, we notice the deacon's *orarium*, or stole, which from ancient times has been their distinctive attire, and symbolizes the yoke of Christ (Matthew 11:28-30) that each deacon takes on in his ministry. Deacons wear the stole over their left shoulder, leaving their right side free to fulfill their active duties as servant of God's people.

Even though Acts 6 records that "they"—all the Apostles—ordained the seven deacons, notice how St. Peter is the central character in this painting, the only Apostle laying on hands and ordaining the deacons. While the figures of the Apostles to his left and the deacons to his right are squeezed into tight crowds, not very defined or individualized, Peter stands out taller than those on either side, and he is represented more robust and true to life. Peter's facial features are more defined, as the artist portrays him in the traditional manner of white hair and short, curly beard. He is the only Apostle pictured with a halo, even though all the Apostles are saints. As we have seen before, Byzantine art uses symbolic rendering to teach, here reminding the viewer of Peter's position as the head of the Apostles, the rock upon whom Jesus builds his Church and to whom he gave the keys of the kingdom (Matthew 16:13-19), and as such Peter represents the unbroken apostolic and priestly authority that is passed down in ordination.

Saint Peter Ordaining the First Deacons / Gianni Dagli Orti / the Art Archive at Art Resource, NY

Just to the left of *Saint Peter Ordaining the First Deacons*, the artist depicts the prophet Joel, who prophesied the outpouring of the Spirit (Joel 2). In one hand Joel holds an open scroll describing the fulfillment of his prophecy. With his other hand Joel gestures to a crowd, which occupies a walled city. This crowd, led by kings and priests, represents the nations who now come to worship the Lord, as the inscription above the city indicates, "[from every] people and nation" (Revelation 5:9-10). Placed next to one another, these images act like a mini filmstrip or panoramic picture recounting how as the number of disciples from every people and nation, Jew and Gentile, grew, the Apostles bestowed a share of their priestly authority on the deacons to assist in caring for the believers and equipping them to go and bring the Gospel to all they meet in the world.

Not only are the symbols in the fresco used to teach, but the painting's placement in the church also gives instruction. Tokali Kilise is called the "Sistine Chapel of Cappadocia" for its fresco cycle, the most elaborate and sophisticated from this period of Byzantine art.

In this section of the church, these two smaller images are part of a larger fresco cycle that includes a figure of St. Luke (the author of the gospel and Acts) holding a scroll with text from Acts describing the day of Pentecost, an image of St. Peter and the Mission of the Apostles, and these are all placed next to a much larger vault image of Pentecost. The Holy Spirit, the focus of the large Pentecost fresco, is the common thread in this series of images. Placed together the viewer is reminded that the same Spirit that was prophesied by Joel and the Old Testament prophets, has been poured out at Pentecost, and has gone out to the ends of the earth, to all peoples and nations, through the Apostles' preaching and teaching, and the witness of Christian believers, and continues to go out to all men and women through the Church, which Christ established on the rock of Peter and the foundation of the Apostles.

Let's close today's reading with a short meditation in which you imagine your own life as a fresco cycle. The large central image is that of Jesus washing the feet of his disciples, you among them, with Jesus' words, "I have given you an example, that you also should do as I have done to you" (John 13:15). Now, you must supply the other images that relate to this image, scenes of service from your life. What do you envision? How can you fill out those scenes with greater detail, with more loving service? Ask the Holy Spirit to impart to you a greater amount of his grace and strength so that the fresco cycle of your life might be filled with numerous and beautiful images.

_____

_____

Christ washing the Disciples' feet / Scala / Art Resource, NY

Take a moment to journal your ideas, questions, or insights about this lesson. Write down thoughts you had that may not have been mentioned in the text or the discussion questions. List any personal applications you got from the lessons. What challenged you the most in the teachings? How might you turn what you've learned into specific action?

_____

_____

_____

_____

_____

_____

_____

_____

_____

_____

_____

_____

_____

_____

_____

_____

_____

_____

_____

SESSION 8

CHARISMS OF THE SPIRIT

OPENING PRAYER

Come Holy Spirit,
fill the hearts of your faithful
and enkindle in them the fire of your love.
Send forth your Spirit
and they shall be created.
And you shall renew the face of the earth.

Let us pray.
O, God, who did instruct the hearts of the faithful
by the light of the Holy Spirit,
grant that by the same Holy Spirit
we may be truly wise
and ever rejoice in his consolation.
Through Christ our Lord.
Amen.

St. Augustine, pray for us.

INTRODUCTION

Last session we looked at how the Spirit works through the leadership of the Church to direct the Church to all truth and to promote unity amongst the faithful. This session we will see that the Holy Spirit not only works from the "top down," but also from the "bottom up," so to speak, by pouring out his gifts, or charisms, on individual members of the Body of Christ that can then be put to the service of others. By freely bestowing unique gifts among various members of the Body of Christ, God ensures that we assist one another on the journey heavenward, giving us an invaluable means by which to serve one another as Christ served. St. Paul tells the Corinthians to "earnestly desire the spiritual gifts" (1 Corinthians 14:1). Let's take a closer look at the concept of charisms so that we too might grow in our desire for them.

CONNECT

Have you ever been told you are gifted in some area? How have you used that gift in the world?

Think of a time you experienced an extraordinary gift in someone else. How did it make you feel?

DISCUSS

PART 1: THE SPIRIT AND HIS GIFTS
Watch the teaching on video. The following is a brief outline of the topics covered.

I. Charisms Appear Immediately in Acts
   A. At Pentecost—tongues, prophecy, evangelization
   B. Throughout Acts—healing, miracles, teaching, preaching, evangelizing, leadership
   C. Charisms part of normal Christian life

II. St. Paul on Charisms (1 Corinthians 12–14)
   A. *Charism*—Greek meaning "gift freely bestowed"
   B. Variety of charisms throughout Scripture
   C. Charisms are supernatural gifts; newly given or enhancement of a natural gift elevated to supernatural level
   D. Supernatural interaction between God and believer in charism's use
   E. Sanctifying grace vs. charism
      1. Sanctifying grace is for own growth in holiness
      2. Charisms are gifts to be put at service of others

F. Charisms teach us to be dependent on one
another, (1 Corinthians 12:17-18)   _____

G. Charisms are not a reward for or measure   _____
of holiness; but holiness does help
prevent/correct abuses in use of charisms   _____

H. Role of leadership is to equip faithful,   _____
including identifying and calling
forth charisms   _____

I. Still higher way... love (1 Corinthians 13);   _____

DISCUSS

1. What is a charism? Can you list some of the charisms that Dr. Healy mentions? Can you share a
time you have seen charisms exercised?

_____

_____

2. What is the difference between a charism and sanctifying grace received at Baptism?

_____

_____

3. What is the role of leadership in the Church regarding charisms? What role do charisms play
in the Body of Christ?

_____

_____

PART 2: CHARISMS IN THE EARLY CHURCH
Watch the video teaching. The following is a brief outline of the topics covered.

I. Church Fathers
A. Charisms expected as normal effect of
sacraments of initiation
B. Irenaeus, *Against Heresies*, 2.32.4: "Those who   _____
are truly his disciples, receiving grace from him,
perform [miracles]..."   _____
C. Tertullian, *On Baptism*, 20: "Ask from the   _____
Lord, that His own special graces and
distributions of gifts may be supplied you"   _____
D. Hilary of Poitiers, *Tract on the Psalms*, 64.14-15: _____
"Experience intense joy...have insight into
mysteries...prophesy and speak with wisdom....   _____
Gifts enter us as a gentle rain. Little by little
they bear abundant fruit"   _____

E. St. Cyril of Jerusalem, *Catechetical Lectures*:
   "Prepare your souls for the reception of the
   heavenly charisms"

_____

_____

F. St. Augustine, *Sermon 38.2*: Speaks of many
   miracles in his own day

_____

G. Vatican II, *Apostolicam Actuositatem, 3
   (Decree on the Apostolate of the Laity):* The right
   and duty to use them in the Church and in the
   world for the good of men and the building
   up of the Church"

_____

_____

H. Pope St. John Paul II, *Veritatis Splendor, 108
   (The Splendor of Truth):* "The gifts which this
   same Spirit bestows and directs like jewels
   to the Church, the Bride of Christ"

_____

_____

II. It Is Time... for Charisms to Be Awakened

_____

DISCUSS

4. What did St. Hilary of Poitiers say about the use of gifts? How do you experience this in your own life?

_____

_____

5. St. Cyril of Jerusalem encouraged new believers to "prepare your souls for the reception of the heavenly charisms." According to Dr. Healy, how are believers to prepare themselves?

_____

_____

6. St. Augustine initially believed that miracles had only been needed in the age of the Apostles for the initial spread of the Gospel, but that they were no longer needed in his own time. Why did he change his mind? How does his experience challenge us today?

_____

_____

PART 3: INSTITUTIONAL AND CHARISMATIC
Watch the video teaching. The following is a brief outline of the topics covered.

I. Two Complementary Ways the Spirit
   Makes the Church Holy
   A. Institutional—from above, through
      hierarchy/sacraments

_____

_____

_____

B. Charismatic—from "below," through every cell
   in body through the charisms he distributes

_____

C. Complementary work of the Spirit
   and not participating in mission of the Church

_____

E. Vatican II reminds believers they receive
   charisms and they are to use them to serve
   the Church (*Lumen Gentium*, 12)

_____

_____

II. How Do We See This in Acts?

_____

A. Prophecy commonly given in Acts

_____

B. Agabus prophesies famine (Acts 11:27-28)

_____

C. St. Paul's arrest prophesied (Acts 21:9-11)

_____

D. Prophecy often for encouragement and
   understanding; prophecy not giving
   new revelation

_____

E. Prophecy used to direct the Church
   (Acts 13:1-4; 16:6-10); do we seek
   God's direction?

_____

F. St. Paul follows direction of Spirit, but also
   reports back and submits his work to the Church

_____

DISCUSS

7. What are the two complementary dimensions of the Church that Dr. Healy discusses?
According to Pope St. John Paul II, why are these two co-essential?

_____

_____

8. What happens when the charismatic dimension is neglected? What can you do to not neglect
the charismatic dimension in your own life and parish?

_____

_____

MEMORY VERSE

"Now there are varieties of gifts, but the same Spirit; and there are varieties of service, but the same Lord; and there are varieties of working, but it is the same God who inspires them all in every one."
—1 Corinthians 12:4-6

CLOSING PRAYER

"To each is given a manifestation of the Spirit for the common good."
—1 Corinthians 12:7

Lord God, through your love and generosity,
you continue to bless your Church
by distributing great and beautiful gifts among us.
Despite our unworthiness, you continue to cherish your sons and daughters,
lavishing us with gifts so that we may share your generosity with the world.
Grant that we may look to your love and kindness as a guide,
never thinking of ourselves, but putting our brothers and sisters first.
Help us to build your Kingdom on earth,
freely and generously sharing the gifts you have uniquely chosen for each of us,
as you have so freely and generously dispensed them
for the benefit of your Body, the Church. Through Christ our Lord. Amen.

St. Augustine, pray for us.

FURTHER READING

Catechism of the Catholic Church, 799-801

Luis Martinez, *True Devotion to the Holy Spirit* **(Sophia Institute Press, 2008)**

COMMIT—DAY 1
CHARISMS

As Dr. Healy discusses, charisms are supernatural gifts, poured out by the Spirit. As the word's Greek root highlights, a charism is a "gift freely bestowed"—not a reward for good works or a proof of holiness, but an unmerited gift. St. Peter makes this clear when after he heals the lame man, Peter says, "Why do you stare at us, as though by our own power or piety we had made him walk?" (Acts 3:12). These gifts may be newly given, or an enhancement of a natural gift

The Holy Spirit © BrankaVV / shutterstock.com

that the Spirit elevates to a supernatural level. Let's take a look at just some of the myriad of charisms listed in Sacred Scripture.

Look up the following verses.	What charisms are noted?
Romans 12:6-8	
1 Corinthians 7:6-9	
1 Corinthians 12:7-10	
1 Corinthians 12:28	
1 Corinthians 13:1-3	
1 Corinthians 14:26-33	
Ephesians 4:11	
1 Peter 4:9-11	

Charisms are distinct from sanctifying grace, which is given at Baptism to make us holy, and includes the seven gifts of the Holy Spirit—wisdom, understanding, counsel, knowledge, piety, fortitude, and fear of the Lord (Isaiah 11:2-3). Sanctifying grace, including the seven gifts of the Holy Spirit, is given for our own personal sanctification, bestowed on us through Baptism, and strengthened as we are confirmed in Christ. The Holy Spirit pours his own life into us through these gifts, enabling us to grow in holiness.

While the goal of sanctifying grace is our own growth in holiness, charisms have a different end or goal: that of building up the Body of Christ. Charisms are distributed among believers according to the needs, not of the believer, but rather, of the community around him. Charisms are given, not primarily for our own use, but for the use of others—for the building up of other members of the Body of Christ.

While each baptized Christian receives all seven gifts of the Holy Spirit at Baptism, the multitude of charisms is distributed disparately throughout the Body of Christ; that is, not every charism is given to each believer. St. Paul explains the reason for this using an analogy. Read 1 Corinthians 12:12-26. Here he compares the members of the Church to the parts of a body. In his analogy, what does Paul say about every part of the whole?

_____

_____

In verses 22-24, what does he say specifically about the weaker or hidden parts?

_____

_____

While the Spirit bestows a variety of charisms throughout the people of God, this myriad of gifts works to unify the Body of Christ, first by teaching us to rely upon one another since no one person possesses all charisms, and also by calling forth our joy and gratitude for the way in which the Spirit pours out these gifts. When God gives another person a particular charism, rather than eliciting jealously, it should bring a response of joy and gratitude because God is blessing us through this brother or sister's charism. Just as the body cannot function fully without its hands, or feet, or eyes, or ears, etc., so too all Christians and their God-given charisms are to be put to use to help the other members.

With these things in mind, go back to the list of charisms you created. Choose two or three charisms from the list and think of someone you've met who exemplifies each particular charism. Don't merely list the name of the person, but provide details as to how you have witnessed each person using their particular charism(s) to serve the Body of Christ. Consider thanking these people for how they serve the Body of Christ by exercising their charisms.

_____

_____

_____

COMMIT—DAY 2
POPE FRANCIS ON CHARISMS

A consistent theme throughout the pontificate of Pope Francis has been the Body of Christ. He speaks often of that interconnection between people, steeped in love, that allows and even obligates us to serve others, particularly those who are materially, spiritually, or emotionally impoverished. To that end, on October 1, 2014, he gave a General Audience that focused on charisms within the Church. Let's explore his words and see if they can illuminate further the concept of charisms in our hearts and minds:

God the Father and the Holy Spirit. / National Trust Photo Library / Art Resource, NY

> *"In the Christian perspective, however, a charism is much more than a personal quality, a predisposition that one can be endowed with: a charism is a grace, a gift bestowed by God the Father, through the action of the Holy Spirit. And it is a gift which is given to someone not because he is better than others or because he deserves it: it is a gift that God gives him, because with his freely given love he can place him in service to the entire community, for the good of all. Speaking in a rather more human way, one says: 'God gives this quality, this charism to this person, not for himself, but in order that he may put it at the service of the whole community.'"*

Are there prerequisites to receiving a charism? Why is this important for us to remember?

_____

_____

How and why are they given?

_____

Pope Francis continues,

> *"The most beautiful experience, though, is the discovery of all the different charisms and all the gifts of his Spirit that the Father showers on his Church! This must not be seen as a reason for confusion, for discomfort: they are all gifts that God gives to the Christian community, in order that it may grow in harmony, in the faith and in his love, as one body, the Body of Christ. The same Spirit who bestows this diversity of charisms unites the Church. It is always the same Spirit. Before this multitude of charisms, our heart, therefore, must open itself to joy and we must think: 'What a beautiful thing! So many different gifts, because we are all God's children, all loved in a unique way.'"*

Look up Ephesians 1:3. How is Pope Francis echoing St. Paul's description of the gifts poured out on the Christian community at Ephesus?

_____

_____

Following St. Paul in his letter to the Corinthians, Dr. Healy points out that God gives each Christian one or more charisms. Pope Francis echoes this by calling us to reflect on the charism(s) the Spirit has given us personally in our own lives, reminding us that it is in the community of believers where we recognize these gifts and where these gifts flourish.

> "An important thing that should be highlighted immediately is the fact that alone, one cannot understand whether one has a charism, and which one. … It is within the community that the gifts the Father showers upon us bloom and flourish; and it is in the bosom of the community that one learns to recognize them as a sign of his love for all his children. So, each one of us should ask him/herself: Is there a charism that the Lord has endowed me with, by the grace of his Spirit, and that my brothers and sisters in the Christian community have recognized and encouraged? And how do I act with regard to this gift: do I use it with generosity, placing it at the service of everyone, or do I overlook it and end up forgetting about it? Or perhaps it becomes a reason for pride in me, such that I always complain about others and insist on getting my way in the community?' These are questions that we must ask ourselves: if there is a charism in me, if this charism is recognized by the Church, if I am happy with this charism or am I a bit jealous of the charisms of others, whether I wanted or I want to have that charism. A charism is a gift: God alone bestows it!"

Recalling the list of charisms from yesterday's Commit Day, take some time to ask yourself the questions posed by Pope Francis. Is there a charism that the Lord has endowed you with, by the grace of his Spirit, and that your brothers and sisters in the Christian community have recognized and encouraged?

_____

_____

How do you act with regard to this gift: do you use it with generosity, placing it at the service of everyone, or do you overlook it?

_____

_____

Has this gift become a reason for pride in you, such that you always complain about others and insist on getting your way in the community?

_____

_____

Take some time to reflect on your answers to these personal questions. Pray that God will help you to recognize your charisms and ask God how you can more effectively use the charism of love to serve your community.

COMMIT—DAY 3
A MORE EXCELLENT WAY

"You know well enough that our Lord does not look so much at the greatness of our actions, nor even at their difficulty, but at the love with which we do them.

—St. Therese of Lisieux

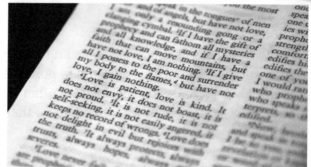

1 Corinthians 13:4 Love is Patient © deepspacedave / shutterstock.com

In St. Paul's First Letter to the Corinthians, at the heart of his teaching on charisms and spiritual gifts, he focuses his readers's attention on the "higher gifts," "a still more excellent way"—love. What at first might appear to be a digression is anything but. Let's take a look at what he says.

> **LECTIO:** The practice of praying with Scripture, *lectio divina*, begins with an active and close reading of the Scripture passage. Read the Scripture passage below and then answer the questions to take a closer look at some of the details of the passage.

"But earnestly desire the higher gifts. And I will show you a still more excellent way. If I speak in the tongues of men and angels, but have not love, I am a noisy gong or a clanging cymbal. And if I have prophetic powers, and understand all mysteries and all knowledge, and if I have all faith, so as to remove mountains, but have not love, I gain nothing. Love is patient and kind; love is not jealous or boastful; it is not arrogant or rude. Love does not insist on its own way; it is not irritable or resentful; it does not rejoice at wrong, but rejoices in the right. Love bears all things, believes all things, hopes all things, endures all things. Love never ends; as for prophecies, they will pass away; as for tongues, they will cease; as for knowledge, it will pass away. For our knowledge is imperfect and our prophecy is imperfect; but when the perfect comes, the imperfect will pass away. When I was a child, I spoke like a child, I thought like a child, I reasoned like a child; when I became a man, I gave up childish ways. For now we see in a mirror dimly, but then face to face. Now I know in part; then I shall understand fully, even as I have been fully understood. So faith, hope, love abide, these three; but the greatest of these is love."

—1 Corinthians 12:31-13:13

To what "higher gifts" is St. Paul referring?

_____

Paul says, "And I will show you a still more excellent way." A "more excellent way" to what?

_____

_____

What will end? What will never end?

_____

_____

> **MEDITATIO:** *Lectio*, a close reading and rereading, is followed by *meditatio*, time to reflect on the Scripture passage and to ponder the reason for particular events, descriptions, details, phrases, and even echoes from other Scripture passages that were noticed during *lectio*. Take some time now to meditate on the Scripture passage from page 147.

That love is central to the use of charisms for the building up of the Church was echoed by Pope Benedict XVI when he said, love "is the fruitful source of all service to the Church, its measure, its method and its verification." Our meditation today is taken from one of his General Audience messages.

> *"Justified through the gift of faith in Christ, we are called to live in the love of Christ for neighbour, because it is on this criterion that we shall be judged at the end of our lives. In reality Paul only repeats what Jesus himself said... . In the First Letter to the Corinthians St. Paul pours himself out in a famous eulogy of love. It is called the 'hymn to love': 'If I speak in the tongues of men and of angels, but have not love, I am a noisy gong or a clanging cymbal.... Love is patient and kind; love is not jealous or boastful; it is not arrogant or rude. Love does not insist on its own way' (1 Cor 13:1, 4-5). Christian love is particularly demanding because it springs from Christ's total love for us: that love that claims us, welcomes us, embraces us, sustains us, to the point of tormenting us since it forces each one to no longer live for himself, closed into his own selfishness, but for him 'who for their sake died and was raised' (2 Cor 5:15). The love of Christ makes us, in him, that new creation (cf. 2 Cor 5:17), which comes to belong to his Mystical Body that is the Church."* —Pope Benedict XVI, General Audience, November 26, 2008

Meditatio often includes reflecting on Scripture in light of other parts of Scripture. Today, spend this meditation time looking at how Jesus showed love in the various noted Scriptures. Then write down how you can imitate these various attributes of Christ's total love in your daily life, and/or how you can exercise your charism(s) with these attributes of love.

Love is...	Christ: A Living Example of Love	How can I imitate Christ's total love in my every day life?
Patient	2 Peter 3:9	
Kind	Mark 6:34-37	
Not boastful	Philippians 2:5-8	
Not arrogant	John 13:1-15	
Not rude	Matthew 11:28-30	
Does not insist on its own way	Matthew 26:39	
Is not irritable	John 18:1-40	
Is not resentful	Luke 23:34	
Does not rejoice at wrong	Matthew 21:12-13	
Rejoices all things	Luke 10:20-24	
Hopes all things	Matthew 19:25-26	
Endures all things	Hebrews 12:2	

ORATIO, CONTEMPLATIO, RESOLUTIO: Having read and meditated on today's Scripture passage, take some time to bring your thoughts to God (*oratio*) and engage God in silence (*contemplatio*). Then end your prayer by making a simple concrete resolution (*resolutio*) to respond to God's prompting of your heart in today's prayer.

Adoration of the Trinity / Scala / Art Resource, NY

COMMIT – DAY 4
INSTITUTIONAL AND CHARISMATIC

In the previous session, we looked at the institutional dimension of the Church. We examined the leadership structure and how through apostolic succession, the Holy Spirit has guided the Church consistently through the ages. In this session, we have examined the charismatic dimension of the Church, how the Holy Spirit works through individuals within the Body of Christ, that all her members might play a vital role in the building and renewal of Christ's Kingdom. One might ask which is more important? The institutional or the charismatic dimension of the Church? The answer is...both.

Old engravings, a priest in the church school from the book "History of the Church" © Sergey Kohl / shutterstock.com

In its *Dogmatic Constitution on the Church, Lumen Gentium,* Vatican II addressed both the institutional and charismatic nature of the Church, and how they work together to build the Body of Christ.

> *"It is not only through the sacraments and the ministries of the Church that the Holy Spirit sanctifies and leads the people of God and enriches it with virtues, but, 'allotting his gifts to everyone according as He wills,' He distributes special graces among the faithful of every rank. By these gifts He makes them fit and ready to undertake the various tasks and offices which contribute toward the renewal and building up of the Church, according to the words of the Apostle: 'The manifestation of the Spirit is given to everyone for profit.' These charisms, whether they be the more outstanding or the more simple and widely diffused, are to be received with thanksgiving and consolation for they are perfectly suited to and useful for the needs of the Church. Extraordinary gifts are not to be [rashly]* sought after, nor are the fruits of apostolic labor to be presumptuously expected from their use; but judgment as to their genuinity and proper use belongs to those who are appointed leaders in the Church, to whose special competence it belongs, not indeed to extinguish the Spirit, but to test all things and hold fast to that which is good."* —Lumen Gentium, 12

[*The Latin word *temere*, which appears in the original document, it best translated as "rashly."]

In addition to "the sacraments and ministries of the Church," how else does the Holy Spirit sanctify and lead the people of God? How are charisms to be received by the faithful?

_____

_____

Who judges as to the genuine nature and proper use of a charism?

_____

_____

151

Vatican II reminds us of the myriad ways in which the Holy Spirit works to bring about holiness in the Church. Whether through the ministries and sacraments of the Church or through her individual members, the Holy Spirit is always at work to serve God's children. By working from the "top down" as well as from the "bottom up," so to speak, the Holy Spirit moves our hearts from both directions, neither of which is mutually exclusive; rather both are complementary and co-essential to the building up of the Body of Christ.

This working of the Holy Spirit "from below" requires a response, and Pope Francis exhorts each of us to let ourselves be led by the Spirit.

> *"Ours is a hopeful perspective, but one which is also demanding. The temptation is always within us to resist the Holy Spirit, because he takes us out of our comfort zone and unsettles us; he makes us get up and drives the Church forward. It is always easier and more comfortable to settle in our sedentary and unchanging ways. In truth, the Church shows her fidelity to the Holy Spirit in as much as she does not try to control or tame him. We Christians become true missionary disciples, able to challenge consciences, when we throw off our defensiveness and allow ourselves to be led by the Spirit. He is freshness, imagination and newness."*
> —Pope Francis, Homily at the Cathedral of the Holy Spirit in Istanbul, November 29, 2014

Why are we tempted to resist the Holy Spirit? How do we become true missionary disciples?

_____

_____

_____

Take some time today to reflect on how you may be resisting the Holy Spirit. How might a greater use of the institutional dimension of the Church (sacraments, etc.) help you to better allow the Holy Spirit to guide you? Pray for openness to the working of the Holy Spirit in your life, your parish, in your community and in your home.

_____

_____

_____

_____

_____

_____

_____

_____

COMMIT–DAY 5
TRUTH AND BEAUTY

Stories of the Beata Umiltà, (Saint Humility Altarpiece),
Pietro Lorenzetti, c. 1340, Galleria Uffizi, Florence, Italy

Stories of the Beata Umilta. (Saint Humility Altarpiece) / Scala / Art Resource, NY

"To each is given the manifestation of the Spirit for the common good."
—1 Corinthians 12:7

Throughout every age, the Lord bestows his charisms and gifts on his Church. We see one example of this in the altarpiece painted by Pietro Lorenzetti, illustrating the life of Beata Umiltà, or St. Humility. The saint is the central figure in the large panel, which is currently surrounded by eleven smaller panels with scenes of her life. In these scenes we see her exercising numerous charisms that the Spirit poured out in her life and that St. Paul describes in 1 Corinthians: preaching, teaching, evangelizing, healing, working miracles (raising a boy from the dead), listening to God and obeying, and displaying great wisdom and knowledge.

Beata Umiltà lived in Italy in the late thirteenth century. She married at fifteen years of age and suffered greatly when her two children died in infancy and her husband began to live a life of dissipation. After an illness that nearly took his life, her husband had a change of heart and entered a monastery, allowing Beata Umiltà, who turned to Jesus in her suffering, to enter a religious order where she continued to live a life of holiness.

Stories of Saint Humility: the Saint Cures the Monk of Sant'Apollinare with the Sign of the Cross / Scala / Art Resource, NY

She was renowned for her sanctity and the gifts the Spirit poured out on her. When a monk of the same order contracted gangrene and was about to have his leg amputated, he insisted that he be brought to Beata Umiltà to have her pray for him. In the panel on the left, we see the monks bringing the sick man on a pallet and climbing the steps to see Beata, perhaps signifying the elevated life that she led. The figures are portrayed in a naturalistic way, expressing emotion: Beata's head is inclined in compassion toward the monk. In her hand is a prayer book, signaling the life of prayer lived by this holy woman. She makes the Sign of the Cross over the monk, fervently praying for his healing—and God grants her request. Pietro Lorenzetti is known for portraying accurate scenes of everyday life, here giving a wonderfully detailed representation of a thirteenth-century building—note the mosaic details on the front steps and the iron circlets for tethering horses on the street level. These circumstantial details advance the narrative and present a credible space to showcase this event.

Stories of the Blessed Umilta: the Saint resuscitating a dead child / Scala / Art Resource, NY

A neighboring panel recounts another of Beata's miracles. A woman comes to the saint with a dead child. Pietro Lorenzetti opens the sidewall of the chapel so that we can see Beata, who has laid the child before the altar, on her knees, hands tightly clasped, praying earnestly to God for the child's life. The corner column of the church is used to separate this scene on the right from the later scene on the left, where we see Beata giving the resurrected child back to his mother; the boy is reaching out to her, emphasizing that he is no longer dead but miraculously raised. The cross over the church entrance and the altar inside the chapel remind the viewer that the healing was not accomplished through any power of Beata Umiltà, but by the power of Jesus Christ. The church architecture that frames the event drives home the point that we must first bring our prayers before the altar of God, before going out to serve the world.

Even though Beata Umiltà longed for solitude, prayer, and contemplation, her superior requested that she become the abbess of a new convent. The panel to the right depicts Beata dictating her discourses to her nuns. She wrote beautiful meditations for the sisters entrusted to her care, which she described as being received directly from the Holy Spirit. She was given a special gift of wisdom to teach and direct her sisters, and many others who came to her for advice. That God gave her gifts to build up his Church is reinforced by the use of a church as the panel's backdrop for Beata's speaking on the holy things of God. Beata Umiltà desired the "higher gifts" and union with God; God, who is never outdone, not only granted her desire, but poured out many other gifts on her for the upbuilding of those around her.

While Beata Umiltà lived in the late thirteenth century, many of the scenes portrayed in this altarpiece could very easily have been episodes taken from the Acts of the Apostles, as the Holy Spirit

Stories of Saint Humility: Saint Humility explaining the Sacred Scriptures / Scala / Art Resource, NY

gave her charisms for healing and miracles, for teaching and formation in faith and holiness. Beata Umiltà's life illustrates that the charisms and gifts of the Spirit are for every age of the Church, for its edification and upbuilding. It is fitting that this work showing Beata Umiltà's life is done as an altarpiece decorating the space behind an altar upon which is celebrated the Mass. In this we see the meeting of the institutional and charismatic dimensions of the Church—Beata Umiltà was nourished and built up by the Body of Christ at the Eucharistic table in Christ's Church, and the Holy Spirit poured out many gifts and charisms in her life so that through her the Body of Christ was built up and extended.

St. Paul tells us to "earnestly desire the higher gifts" (1 Corinthians 12:31). Pray today that you would desire the higher gifts with a new earnestness like St. Humility.

Take a moment to journal your ideas, questions, or insights about this lesson. Write down thoughts you had that may not have been mentioned in the text or the discussion questions. List any personal applications you got from the lessons. What challenged you the most in the teachings? How might you turn what you've learned into specific action?

_____

_____

_____

_____

_____

_____

_____

_____

_____

_____

_____

_____

_____

_____

_____

_____

_____

_____

_____

SESSION 9

JOY IN PERSECUTION

OPENING PRAYER

Come Holy Spirit,
fill the hearts of your faithful
and enkindle in them the fire of your love.
Send forth your Spirit
and they shall be created.
And you shall renew the face of the earth.

Let us pray.
O, God, who did instruct the hearts of the faithful
by the light of the Holy Spirit,
grant that by the same Holy Spirit
we may be truly wise
and ever rejoice in his consolation.
Through Christ our Lord.
Amen.

Sts. Perpetua and Felicity, pray for us.

INTRODUCTION

Last session, we looked at how the Holy Spirit freely bestows his gifts upon those who are redeemed through Baptism and how these gifts permanently dispose believers toward the promptings of the Holy Spirit for the purpose of building up the Church. In this session, we will delve into the gift of fortitude and discover how that gift, perfected by the fruit of joy, equips us to face persecution with an abiding joy of the Lord in our hearts. Joy in persecution—is this included in Jesus' exhortation that those who wanted to be his disciples must deny themselves, pick up their cross, and follow him?

CONNECT

Do you personally know people who have been persecuted for their beliefs? What were the circumstances, and how did they respond? Do you think they wanted revenge, or did they willingly forgive their persecutors? Where did they find strength to forgive and carry on?

What do you think when you hear news stories of Christians around the world or even in our own country being persecuted or martyred for their beliefs? How do you respond?

DISCUSS

PART 1: CONFORMED TO JESUS CHRIST
Watch the teaching on video. The following is a brief outline of the topics covered.

I. Early Christians' Response to Persecution
   A. Remembered Jesus' teaching
   (Luke 6:21-23)
   B. "Rejoice ... and leap for joy"

II. Examples in Acts
   A. "Left the presence of the council, rejoicing"
   (Acts 5:28-29, 40-41)
   B. Stephen, first martyr, "his face was like
   the face of an angel" (Acts 6:15)
   C. Deepest work of Holy Spirit is to conform us
   to Jesus; to reproduce the pattern of his life
   D. Stephen's offering of his suffering in union
   with Jesus wins grace for Paul

DISCUSS

1. In Matthew 5:10-12 and Luke 6:22-23, Jesus teaches his disciples about persecution. Why should Jesus' disciples expect to be persecuted (John 15:18-20)? Have you ever been persecuted/ridiculed for your faith? How did you respond?

_____

_____

2. What does Jesus command us to do for our enemies and persecutors (Matthew 5:44.)? Why? How is St. Stephen a witness to Jesus' teaching? How do the stories of the martyrs encourage us?

_____

_____

3. Is our Christian faith meant to be a private matter? Why or why not?

_____

_____

PART 2: JESUS' LIFE IN STS. PETER AND PAUL
Watch the video teaching. The following is a brief outline of the topics covered.

I. Jesus' Life Fulfills Old Testament Types
   A. Jesus pre-figured by Moses, David, Solomon, Jonah, temple, manna, Suffering Servant, etc.
   B. "This Scripture ... fulfilled in your hearing" (Luke 4:21)
   C. On road to Emmaus, everything written must be fulfilled (Luke 24:13-35)
   D. God orders all events of salvation history so that they point forward to the fullness of his plan

II. Jesus' Life Also Points Forward
   A. Present in the members of his Body; disciples "post-figure" Jesus; Jesus is the center point
   B. St. Peter's imprisonment recalls Jesus
     1. At Passover, by a Herod
     2. Arrested, handed over, guarded, unclothed
     3. Angel, bright light, get up (arise), passes through locked doors
     4. First seen by a woman, thought to be a spirit
     5. Disciples in upper room unable to believe

6. Deepest work of Holy Spirit is to reproduce in us the life of Jesus

C. St. Paul's sufferings recall Jesus

  1. Praising God helps us in times of trial

  2. Three times Paul's sufferings are predicted

  3. Paul's friends try to prevent his suffering

  4. "Ready to die for the Lord"; Peter fails before Pentecost, but Paul succeeds after being filled with the Spirit

  5. "Thy will be done"

  6. Accused of defiling Temple, brought before Sanhedrin, at time of Passover, brought before Roman governor, Felix, and Herod

  7. Jews accuse Paul, chief priests seek death

DISCUSS

4. As Dr. Healy explains in the video, how is Jesus the center of God's plan of salvation?

_____

_____

_____

5. According to Dr. Healy, why does St. Peter fail at first in his declaration of faith to Jesus, while St. Paul succeeds?

_____

_____

_____

6. Have you ever thought of your life as "post-figuring" Jesus' life? In what areas have you done this well? In what areas do you need to ask the Holy Spirit to help reproduce the life of Jesus in you?

_____

_____

_____

PART 3: THE WITNESS OF MARTYRDOM

Watch the video teaching. The following is a brief outline of the topics covered.

I. Martyrdom
    A. *martyria*—Greek for testimony,
       martys—one who gives witness
    B. Martyrdom is a great victory
       (Revelation 12:10-11)
    C. Pope St. John Paul II: "The martyr...is a sign of
       that greater love which sums up all other
       values ..." (*Incarnationis Mysterium*, 13)
    D. Martyrdom always a possibility for any disciple
    E. Interior belief and exterior confession
       (Romans 10:10)

II. Early Martyrs
    A. St. Polycarp, bishop of Smyrna; "The spectator
       saw ... not flesh burning, but bread baking"
    B. St. Ignatius of Antioch; "I am the wheat
       of God ... ground by the teeth of wild beasts"
    C. Sts. Perpetua and Felicity; noble woman
       and her maid, "But then there will be
       another in me who will suffer for me"

III. Martyrs for Today
    A. St. John Baptist—sanctity of marriage
    B. Sts. Thomas More and John Fischer—
       church authority over state
    C. Maria Goretti—chastity
    D. Pope Pius XI: "Let us thank God that he
       makes us live among the present problems.
       It is no longer permitted to anyone
       to be mediocre."

DISCUSS

7. Why did the early Church call those who gave their lives for the faith martyrs? What did martyrdom signify for them?

_____

_____

8. How should we look at the possibility of martyrdom today? (See Revelation 12:10-12 and Romans 10:10.)

_____

_____

9. Dr. Healy gives several accounts of martyrdom. Which one moves you the most? Why? How do you think these martyrs were able to persevere in the faith to the point of death (Galatians 2:20)?

_____

_____

MEMORY VERSE

"They have conquered him [the accuser] by the blood of the Lamb and by the word of their testimony, for they loved not their lives even unto death." —**Revelation 12:11**

CLOSING PRAYER

O God, who by the witness in word
and deed of your many martyrs
has brought faith to countless souls
throughout the centuries,
grant us a share of their courage and joy.
By their intercession
may we daily pick up our cross and follow Christ.
We ask this through our Lord Jesus Christ,
your Son, who lives and reigns with you,
in the union of the Holy Spirit,
one God forever and forever.
Amen.

Sts. Perpetua and Felicity, pray for us

FURTHER READING

Pope Benedict XVI, *Jesus*, "The Apostles and the Early Church," *This Rock* magazine, April 2007, Volume 18, Number 4

Eusebius of Caesarea, *The History of the Martyrs in Palestine*

Catechism of the Catholic Church, 2471-2474

COMMIT—DAY 1
THE WITNESS OF THE MARTYRS

The word "martyr" comes from the Greek word *martyria*, literally "witness" or "testimony," and one who gave witness or testified was a *martys*. In ancient Greece, *martys* was used to denote someone, a spectator, who gave an authoritative account, often within the Greek legal system. In the early Church, the Apostles are martyrs first and foremost because they are witnesses to Jesus Christ's teaching and life, his words and deeds, and they give an authoritative account of this in their preaching and teaching. As the Apostles and disciples endure persecution leading to death, the emphasis of martyrdom becomes increasingly focused on the suffering and death endured for giving that witness or testimony.

Christian Martyrs Entering the Amphitheater / © RMN-Grand Palais / Art Resource, NY

The intent of those who persecuted the Apostles and early Christians, whether the Jewish religious authorities, such as Saul when he oversaw St. Stephen's stoning, or the Roman state, such as Nero who had St. Peter crucified and St. Paul beheaded, is to end Christianity's growing presence. Thus Saul quickly headed to Damascus to arrest followers of the Way, hoping to stop their testimony and the conversions among the Jewish community there. Numerous Roman emperors hoped to snuff out the Christian religion, returning its adherents to participation in the Roman cult. But rather than stamping out Christianity or convincing the Christians to forsake their testimony, the repeated horrific persecutions fuel its growth. As one early Christian apologist describes,

> "Do you not see them exposed to wild beasts, that they may be persuaded to deny the Lord, and yet not overcome? Do you not see that the more of them are punished, the greater becomes the number of the rest? This does not seem to be the work of man: this is the power of God; these are the evidences of His manifestation."
> —*Epistle to Diognetus*, 7

Or as Justin Martyr (c. AD 100-165) writes,

> "For it is plain that, though beheaded, and crucified, and thrown to wild beasts, and chains, and fire, and all other kinds of torture, we do not give up our confession; but the more such things happen, the more do others and in larger numbers become faithful, and worshippers of God through the name of Jesus. For just as if one should cut away the fruit-bearing parts of a vine, it grows up again, and yields other branches flourishing and fruitful; even so the same thing happens with us."
> —*Dialogue with Trypho*, 110

This phenomenon, that as the number of martyrs increases, the number of believers also increases all the more, goes against all pagan reasoning. As Tertullian describes, instead of ending Christianity, "We multiply wherever we are mown down by you: the blood of Christians is seed...." (*Apology*, 50). The blood of those who "loved not their lives even unto death" (Revelation 12:11) is a seed that brings forth a hundredfold yield; a seed that works much like the tiny mustard seed in Jesus' parable that grows into a great tree. And this seed brings an incredible abundance of God's grace and an outpouring of the Spirit on the Church. That this would be the case is already foreseen in the Old Testament. In the second century BC, Antiochus Epiphanes IV, in an attempt to compel the Jews to abandon their faith and adopt the Hellenist religion, converts the Jewish Temple to the worship of the Greek god Zeus and forces Jews to forsake the Torah and eat unclean foods or face death. This persecution gives rise to a revolt led by Judas Maccabeus; against all odds, the Jews take back control of Jerusalem and rededicate the Temple. When we look at the account of this conflict recorded in 1 and 2 Maccabees, we find that the unexpected success of the Maccabean revolt comes after the witness, suffering, and martyrdom of numerous faithful Jews.

The aged Eleazar courageously chooses a painful death rather than save his life through cowardice and capitulation, desiring to "leave to the young a noble example of how to die a good death willingly and nobly for the revered and holy laws" (2 Maccabees 6:28). A mother and her seven sons are one by one brutally tortured and executed, but as the youngest son is to die he proclaims, "I, like my brothers, give up body and life for the laws of our fathers, appealing to God to show mercy soon to our nation" (2 Maccabees 7:37). And God does show his mercy soon as others are encouraged to remain faithful and the rag-tag revolt led by Judas Maccabeus wins victory after victory against their persecutors.

Read 2 Maccabees 6:18-31, the account of Eleazar, or 2 Maccabees 7, the account of the mother and her seven sons. What inspires you most about their faithful witness? What do you think is the source of their fortitude and courage? How does their faithfulness inspire you to give public witness to the Faith in your own life?

_____

_____

_____

The same mercy won by Eleazar and the mother and her seven sons is poured out on the Church, alongside the gift of the Holy Spirit. Thus in the Acts of Apostles we see a similar effect from St. Stephen's suffering and martyrdom. Stephen gives witness to Jesus Christ in his preaching and teaching. Then as he is being stoned, Stephen prays, "Lord, do not hold this sin against them" (Acts 7:60). This prayer bears incredible fruit when Saul, the man who oversaw Stephen's stoning, receives a vision of Christ himself and as a result repents and comes to believe in Jesus Christ. And then later when St. Paul's preaching in Philippi results in Paul and Silas suffering many blows and imprisonment, the jailor and his household will come to faith because of the witness of Paul and Silas (Acts 16:22-33).

Such accounts are repeated over and over and resound throughout the Church's history, bearing witness to Tertullian's claim that the blood of the martyrs is the seed of the Church.

COMMIT—DAY 2
REJOICE AND LEAP FOR JOY

Early in the Acts of the Apostles we read the unexpected response of the Apostles to the suffering they received at the hands of the Jewish authorities:

> *"[W]hen they had called in the apostles, they beat them and charged them not to speak in the name of Jesus, and let them go. Then they left the presence of the council, rejoicing that they were counted worthy to suffer dishonor for the name."*
>
> —Acts 5:40-41

We see a similar response at other times in Acts. Look up the following verses. How do the Apostles and disciples respond to the suffering they meet?

Acts 13:48-52 _____

Acts 16:23-25 _____

Colossians 1:24 _____

St. James opens his epistle with the exhortation, "Count it all joy, my brethren, when you meet various trials" (James 1:2). Rejoicing! Counting it all joy! This response of Jesus Christ's disciples to suffering, repeated in their words and deeds, finds its origin in Jesus'own words. Jesus taught his disciples,

> *"Blessed are you when men hate you, and when they exclude you and revile you, and cast out your name as evil, on account of the Son of man! Rejoice in that day, and leap for joy, for behold, your reward is great in heaven."* —Luke 6:22-23

This response of joy in the midst of persecution is not natural to our fallen human nature. How can we possibly "leap for joy" when we are hated and excluded and reviled? How can suffering dishonor and physical pain result in rejoicing? Natural or not, easy or not, this is the response to which Jesus calls us.

Such a response is possible only through the grace of God operating in our lives and hearts. What gifts are we given by the Holy Spirit to enable us to bear suffering with joy?

_____

_____

_____

The early Church endured much suffering with incredible joy by God's grace. Three things in particular helped them endure. First was the example of Jesus Christ their Lord. Jesus instructed the Apostles that the disciple was not greater than the teacher, and these disciples knew the suffering of their Teacher and Lord. So Peter writes in his first epistle, "For to this you have been called, because Christ also suffered for you, leaving you an example, that you should follow in his steps" (1 Peter 2:21). This understanding, that the disciple was to follow his Lord's example, explains why St. Ignatius, looking ahead to his martyrdom, writes, "Then shall I truly be a disciple of Christ" (*Epistle to the Romans*, 5). Jesus, the Teacher and Lord, had changed the lives of his disciples, and there was nothing more joyful for them than to follow his example.

Second, the early Christians understood that suffering had the ability to produce its own fruit in their lives. Look up the following verses. What does suffering show us? What are the fruits produced by suffering?

Romans 5:3-5 _____

2 Thessalonians 1:4-5 _____

James 1:2-4 _____

1 Peter 1:6-7 _____

The Martyrdom of St. Stephen pediment of the front door of the Saint Etienne du Mont Church, Paris © Zvonimir Atletic / shutterstock.com

Third, the early Christians understood that suffering and martyrdom was not the last word, not the end of the story. The Apostles had witnessed not only Jesus' suffering and Death, but also his glorious Resurrection and Ascension into Heaven. They trusted Jesus' words that he had gone ahead to prepare a place for them, and that they would share in his glory. Just before St. Stephen is dragged out of the city and stoned to death, we are told that he "gazed into heaven and saw the glory of God, and Jesus standing at the right hand of God" (Acts 7:55). Stephen looked heavenward, where he knew Jesus Christ reigned in glory, ready to suffer in imitation of his Lord and join him in Heaven. Thus St. Peter says, "But rejoice in so far as you share Christ's sufferings, that you may also rejoice and be glad when his glory is revealed" (1 Peter 4:13). And St. Paul writes, "I consider that the sufferings of this present time are not worth comparing with the glory that is to be revealed to us" (Romans 8:18).

The early Christians remembered Jesus' teaching and example, and they rejoiced and leapt for joy, even in the face of suffering and martyrdom.

St. Peter and the Apostles' continuing proclamation of Christ crucified agitates the Jewish leaders. The situation escalates, and Herod has James killed. When he sees that this pleases the Jews, he proceeds to arrest Peter also.

LECTIO: The practice of praying with Scripture, *lectio divina*, begins with an active and close reading of the Scripture passage. Read the Scripture passage below and then answer the questions to take a closer look at some of the details of the passage.

"And when [Herod Agrippa I] had seized [Peter], he put him in prison, and delivered him to four squads of soldiers to guard him, intending after the Passover to bring him out to the people. So Peter was kept in prison; but earnest prayer for him was made to God by the church. The very night when Herod was about to bring him out, Peter was sleeping between two soldiers, bound with two chains, and sentries before the door were guarding the prison; and behold, an angel of the Lord appeared, and a light shone in the cell; and he struck Peter on the side and woke him, saying, 'Get up quickly.' And the chains fell off his hands. And the angel said to him, 'Dress yourself and put on your sandals.' And he did so. And he said to him, 'Wrap your mantle around you and follow me.' And he went out and followed him; he did not know that what was done by the angel was real, but thought he was seeing a vision. When they had passed the first and the second guard, they came to the iron gate leading into the city. It opened to them of its own accord, and they went out and passed on through one street; and immediately the angel left him. And Peter came to himself, and said, 'Now I am sure that the Lord has sent his angel and rescued me from the hand of Herod and from all that the Jewish people were expecting.' When he realized this, he went to the house of Mary, the mother of John whose other name was Mark, where many were gathered together and were praying. And when he knocked at the door of the gateway, a maid named Rhoda came to answer. Recognizing Peter's voice, in her joy she did not open the gate but ran in and told that Peter was standing at the gate. They said to her, 'You are mad.' But she insisted that it was so. They said, 'It is his angel!' But Peter continued knocking; and when they opened, they saw him and were amazed. But motioning to them with his hand to be silent, he described to them how the Lord had brought him out of the prison." —Acts 12:4-17

Which details about St. Peter's imprisonment recall Jesus? What are they?

_____

What kind of security does Herod use to secure Peter? How many measures are taken?

_____

Twice the passage says that Herod intends to "bring Peter out." How does Peter describe his rescue?

_____

> **MEDITATIO:** *Lectio*, a close reading and rereading, is followed by *meditatio*, time to reflect on the Scripture passage and to ponder the reason for particular events, descriptions, details, phrases, and even echoes from other Scripture passages that were noticed during *lectio*. Take some time now to meditate on the verse from page 167.

The following meditation is taken from Pope Benedict XVI's General Audience on May 9, 2012:

> *"I would also like to highlight another aspect of Peter's attitude in prison. In fact, we note that while the Christian community is praying earnestly [for] him, Peter 'was sleeping' (Acts 12:6). In a critical situation of serious danger, it is an attitude that might seem strange, but instead denotes tranquility and faith. He trusts God. He knows he is surrounded by the solidarity and prayers of his own people and completely abandons himself into the hands of the Lord. So it must be with our prayer, assiduous, in solidarity with others, fully trusting that God knows us in our depths and takes care of us to the point that Jesus says 'even the hairs of your head are all numbered. Fear not, therefore' (Mt 10:30-31). Peter lives through that night of imprisonment and release from prison as a moment of his discipleship with the Lord who overcomes the darkness of night and frees him from the chains of slavery and the threat of death. ... Once again the community's response to difficulty and danger is to trust in God, strengthening the relationship with Him."*

Pope Benedict XVI's own *lectio*, noting the detail that Peter "was sleeping," draws our attention to Peter's incredible trust in the midst of suffering. Look up the following passages that likely came to mind for St. Peter in his imprisonment. Try memorizing one this week so that you can recall it in times of struggle.

The Liberation of Saint Peter / Scala / Art Resource, NY

Psalm 56:3-4 _____

_____

_____

Psalm 91:1-2_____

_____

_____

Proverbs 3:5-6 _____

Proverbs 29:25 _____

Despite all of Herod's precautions in imprisoning Peter, none of these measures prove an effective barrier to the angel of the Lord. It is the hand of God that has power, not the hand of Herod. What does this truth tell you about the obstacles you may be encountering in following Christ and evangelizing others? Where should your focus be (See 1 John 4:4)?

_____

_____

What does this passage tell you about the power and promise of intercessory prayer?
Ask God to show you who is in most need of your prayers right now to remain faithful to the calling of Christ. Take time to pray for that person now and in the next days.

_____

_____

ORATIO, CONTEMPLATIO, RESOLUTIO: Having read and meditated on today's Scripture passage, take some time to bring your thoughts to God (*oratio*) and engage God in silence (*contemplatio*). Then end your prayer by making a simple concrete resolution (*resolutio*) to respond to God's prompting of your heart in today's prayer.

_____

_____

_____

COMMIT–DAY 4
"OFFER IT UP"

The Church venerates those who pay the ultimate price of martyrdom. Immediately after celebrating Christmas, the Nativity of the Lord, on December 25, the very next day, on December 26, the Church, in the Roman Rite, observes the feast day of St. Stephen, acknowledged as the first Christian martyr. On December 28, the Solemnity of the Holy Innocents is observed, remembering the price paid by those children, and the sorrow of their parents, when Herod slaughtered the infants in Bethlehem in an effort to destroy the "newborn king." The following day, December 29, the feast day of St. Thomas Becket is observed, the Archbishop of Canterbury, England, who was murdered by agents of King Henry II for his defense of the rights of the Church. Why does the Church in her liturgical calendar follow the joyful feast of Christmas with these feasts of martyrdom? The Church reminds us that Jesus took on our human nature, took bodily form, in order to offer his life on the Cross for our salvation, and those who follow him must be willing to imitate him to the end.

Look at your Church calendar and estimate the number of saints venerated as martyrs each year. What do you find significant about this number?

_____

_____

Martyrdom is not a relic from days gone by. An estimated 70 million Christians have been martyred since AD 33. Over half of these were martyred during the twentieth century alone. Since the turn of this century, about one million additional martyrs have given up their lives for Christ in the first ten years alone. These figures exclude the latest atrocities wrought against Christians by extremist groups such as ISIS in the Middle East. Are you surprised by the magnitude of these numbers? What do they suggest about the real possible of facing martyrdom?

_____

_____

Even if physical martyrdom, sometimes referred to as "blood martyrdom," is a remote possibility, martyrdom from esteem of the world, or "white martyrdom," may be a very real prospect. In our increasingly secular world, every time we stand for Christ, we face the possibility of retribution from those who do not agree with our position. It may be as simple as refusing an invitation to view a movie we deem inappropriate, or defending life from conception to natural death, or explaining the Church's teaching on sexuality and marriage, etc. We face the risk of ruptured relationships with friends or family. Or, it might be as dire as facing financial ruin or public defamation and humiliation for taking a principled stand. Are we ready to face these possibilities for following Christ?

Regardless of the type of martyrdom, we are all called to participate in Jesus Christ's sacrifice on the Cross. The *Catechism* reminds us,

> "The cross is the unique sacrifice of Christ, the 'one mediator between God and men.' But because in his incarnate divine person he has in some way united himself to every man, 'the possibility of being made partners, in a way known to God, in the paschal mystery' is offered to all men."
>
> —CCC 618

Having become part of the royal priesthood by our Baptism, we are called to also participate in Christ's Paschal Mystery and offer sacrifice. As lay men and women, how do we do this? St. Paul gives us an answer when he says, "Present your bodies as a living sacrifice, holy and acceptable to God, which is your spiritual worship" (Romans 12:1).

Many of us have heard the expression "offer it up!" This is not just some pious platitude; rather it embodies the principal of offering "our bodies as a living sacrifice" in imitation of Christ. We can join our sufferings and sacrifices to those of Christ's on the Cross as an offering for the merit of others. As Paul says in 2 Corinthians 1:6, "If we are afflicted, it is for your comfort and salvation." In this way, no suffering is ever wasted, and we can trust that in everything "God works for good with those who love him" (Romans 8:28). By offering up our sufferings and making even small sacrifices for others, we participate in Christ's sacrifice and live out Jesus' command to "love one another; even as I have loved you..." (John 13:34).

These offerings, along with the effort and sacrifices that we make to live a holy life filled with good deeds, prepare us to always say "yes" in obedience to God's will, even if it means laying down our lives. As the third-century North African bishop Commodianus describes,

> "Many are the martyrdoms which are made without shedding of blood. ... Since, O son, you desire martyrdom, hear. Be as Abel was, or as Isaac himself, or Stephen, who chose for himself on the way the righteous life. You indeed desire that which is a matter suited for the blessed. First of all, overcome the evil one with your good acts by living well; and when He your King shall see you, be secure. ...Even now, if you have conquered by good deeds, you are a martyr in Him. You, therefore, who seek to extol martyrdom with your word, in peace clothe yourself with good deeds, and be secure."
>
> —On Christian Discipline, 48, 62

Suffering is not something we should fear, but a sure school in which we learn to imitate Christ. The Letter to the Hebrews tells us that Jesus "learned obedience through what he suffered" (Hebrews 5:8). If this was true for the Son of God, who was without sin, how much more should we desire to be tutored in this same method of instruction?

Take some time to reflect on a sacrifice that you can make today, for your own or someone else's growth in holiness.

_____

_____

COMMIT—DAY 5
TRUTH AND BEAUTY

Martyrdom of St. Lawrence,
fifth century, Mausoleum of Galla Placidia, Ravenna, Italy

Lunette with Saint Lawrence. Early Christian mosaic. Scala / Art Resource, NY

This mosaic of the *Martyrdom of St. Lawrence* is found in Ravenna, Italy, in the Mausoleum of Galla Placidia, where the body of the Roman empress and daughter of the Roman Emperor Theodosius I was interred. The Emperor of the Western Roman Empire moved the capital from Milan to Ravenna in the early fifth century, transforming a backwater town into a beautiful city with buildings commensurate with its dignity as capital of the Western Roman Empire. The mausoleum was part of the redecoration program of Ravenna and its ceiling and the upper portion of its walls are covered in stunning mosaics, still beautifully preserved.

Martyred during the persecutions by Emperor Valerian in AD 258, Lawrence was one of the seven deacons who served the church in Rome. A close confidante of St. Sixtus II, he was responsible for the treasury of the Church and the distribution of alms among the poor as archdeacon of the Church of Rome. During Mass at one of the catacombs, Sixtus II was captured and martyred. Perhaps knowing of Lawrence's status as archdeacon, the prefect of Rome demanded that Lawrence turn over to him the treasures of the Church. Lawrence asked for three days in which to gather the treasure; during this period, he gave away as much of the Church property as possible. On the third day, Lawrence came before the emperor and presented the poor, the crippled, the blind, and the suffering and said that these were the true treasures of the Church. This zealous act of defiance directly led to his martyrdom. The prefect, so angry at having been cheated out of the Church's money, ordered Lawrence to be put immediately to death, roasted on a flaming gridiron. The saint, ever cheerful and joyful even amidst such suffering, is reported to have quipped during the torture, "I'm well done. Turn me over!"

The main theme of the mausoleum's mosaic decoration is redemption: victory over death by means of the Cross of Jesus Christ. The mausoleum itself is cruciform in shape. The center of the cupola, the small dome in the middle of the mausoleum, is decorated with a glittering mosaic of the Cross. The cross stands immovable in the midst of hundreds of shimmering stars, which seem to move in concentric circles around it. These are surrounded by the symbols of the Four Evangelists in the corners who also appear in motion, further drawing the viewer's eye to the center image of the cross, the means of our redemption and the gateway to eternal life. This section of the mosaic is created in gold to emphasize the heavenly realm of the triumph of the cross. The glory of the cross shines on the surrounding mosaics as well as the sarcophagi of those interred below.

Interior with vault decorated with mosaics of stars cross and symbols of 4 Evangelists / Alfredo Dagli Orti / The Art Archive at Art Resource, NY

Mosaic with cup and two doves / Alfredo Dagli Orti / The Art Archive at Art Resource, NY

Immediately below this mosaic we see four sets of Apostles dressed as Roman senators, in the posture of acclaiming an emperor; however, the Apostles hail not the emperor, but the Cross of Christ. They all wear white flowing togas and above their heads are shell-shaped canopies. The seashell was a symbol of rebirth often found in Roman mausoleums, perhaps used here as a reminder that the Apostles, all martyrs except John, are reborn in Christ and already enjoying new life in the Heavenly Jerusalem. At their feet are pairs of doves drinking from urns of water, symbolizing the water of Baptism in which the souls of the faithful are reborn. The pattern of vines beneath the doves signifies the fruit of the Eucharist. Together, the Sacraments of Baptism and the Eucharist mark one for Christ, open up the gates to eternal life, and anticipate the banquet of Heaven.

Lunette mosaic with Martyrdom of Saint Lawrence / Alfredo Dagli Orti / The Art Archive at Art Resource, NY

Lunette mosaic with detail of the Good Shepherd / Alfredo Dagli Orti / The Art Archive at Art Resource, NY

The mosaic of the *Martyrdom of St. Lawrence* fits perfectly within the mausoleum's iconographic program of the victory of the Cross. The martyr carries a processional cross, resting upon his right shoulder, and holds a book of the Psalms in his left hand, reminding us of his role in the liturgy as a deacon. There is a strong impression of movement: Lawrence hurries toward the means of his death, the gridiron, white robe flapping as he runs joyfully to his martyrdom. The flames under the gridiron are flickering with animation, further emphasizing the action in this unfolding drama. The dynamism of this mosaic highlights Lawrence's eager willingness to give up his life as a witness to Christ.

The Christian martyr imitates and relives not only the life of Christ, but also his Death; fully living out Jesus' call to "take up [your] cross, and follow me" (Matthew 16:24). It is fitting that directly across from the mosaic of the *Martyrdom of St. Lawrence* is a mosaic of *Jesus the Good Shepherd*. Jesus watches over his flock, caring for their needs, including St. Lawrence and all of the faithful. Jesus holds a cross, echoing that of St. Lawrence's, but his is a shepherd's staff. Even though Lawrence is going to his death (martyred in his thirty-third year, the same age as Jesus at his Crucifixion), Jesus sustains him and awaits him in the Heavenly Kingdom, symbolized by this scene of paradise.

Consider the plan of this mausoleum: the victory of the Cross, by which Christ accomplished our redemption. How do we, like the Apostles, acclaim the Cross? How can we, like St. Lawrence, willingly and joyfully give all to Jesus in self-sacrificial love? How does knowing that our Good Shepherd is carefully watching over us and protecting us help us to more easily live out our call to daily "take up [our] cross"?

_____

_____

SESSION 10

THE BELLY OF THE BEAST

OPENING PRAYER

Come Holy Spirit,
fill the hearts of your faithful
and enkindle in them the fire of your love.
Send forth your Spirit and they shall be created.
And you shall renew the face of the earth.

Let us pray.
O, God, who did instruct the hearts of the faithful
by the light of the Holy Spirit,
grant that by the same Holy Spirit
we may be truly wise
and ever rejoice in his consolation.
Through Christ our Lord.
Amen.

St. Paul, pray for us.

INTRODUCTION

As one of the preeminent Jews of the time, Saul had been zealous in his persecution of Christians. But after he encounters Jesus Christ, St. Paul becomes as zealous in his desire to build Christ's Church as he once was to destroy it. This session we look at the concluding chapters of Acts and join Paul as he journeys to Athens, Corinth and Ephesus, and ultimately to Rome in chains—but not discouraged—continuing to preach Christ crucified to anyone who would listen. The environments in which he preaches are not particularly sympathetic to Christians and the Gospel of Jesus Christ. But that doesn't stop him from evangelizing right at the heart of some of the greatest centers of intellectual influence, political power, and sexual immorality. Our own culture seems to grow more hostile toward Christianity by the day. No doubt we can gain much insight from Paul on how to share the gospel message and remain steadfast despite ever-increasing challenges to our faith. Let's look at his experiences and see what we can learn.

CONNECT

Think about all the people you interact with in your daily life: family, friends, colleagues, a boss, the parish priest, and even the person at the checkout counter in the grocery store. Do you conduct yourself differently depending on the audience, and if so, why? (Consider your vocabulary, choice of dress, and body language, for example.) In what ways are you the same regardless of your audience?

Have you ever been on a trip where virtually nothing went according to plan? Share your experience with the group and discuss how you reacted to your situation.

DISCUSS

PART 1: ST. PAUL IN ATHENS
Watch the teaching on video. The following is a brief outline of the topics covered.

I. Jesus' Words to St. Peter:
   "The gates of hell will not prevail" (Matthew 16:18)
   A. Gates are defensive weapon
   B. Church playing offense; bringing victory
      dismantling evil, liberating captives

II. St. Paul in Athens (Acts 17)
   A. St. Paul adjusts for his audience
      1. Jews—showed how Jesus fulfills Scripture
      2. Gentiles—starts by explaining there is a
         creator God

B. Athens
   1. Leading intellectual center of
      Greco-Roman world _____
   2. Birthplace of philosophy—Socrates,
      Plato, Aristotle _____
   3. Greek arts and science; Roman technology
      —roads, aqueducts, military _____
   4. But spiritual emptiness _____
C. St. Paul's Mission in Athens _____
   1. Stirred up to zeal for lost sheep _____
   2. Begins in synagogue; then city square _____
   3. Encounters Epicureans
      (avoid pain; seek pleasure) and Stoics
      (world is divine) _____
   4. Paul preaches at Mars Hill (Areopagus) _____
      a. Finds something to affirm _____
      b. Teaches doctrine of creation _____
      c. Quotes Greek authors/poets _____
      d. Attacks error of idolatry _____
      e. Once hear truth, now is time to repent _____
      f. Preaches resurrection, repugnant
         to Greeks _____
   5. Divided reaction; faithfulness, not success _____
D. What Do We Learn? _____
   1. Paul proactively seeks the lost _____
   2. Paul found common starting point _____
   3. Not afraid to speak hard parts of the Gospel _____
      (then Resurrection; now judgment) _____

DISCUSS

1. What does "the gates of hell will not prevail" actually mean in Scripture?

_____

_____

2. Who were the Epicureans and the Stoics? What did they believe, and where can their beliefs be found in the world today?

_____

_____

3. How did St. Paul adjust his message to reach different audiences? How might you find common ground with unbelievers today?

_____

_____

> **PART 2: ST. PAUL IN CORINTH AND EPHESUS**
> *Watch the video teaching. The following is a brief outline of the topics covered.*

I. Corinth (Acts 18)
   A. Las Vegas of its time; cosmopolitan
   B. Meeting place of many religions and cults
   C. Chief shrine: Aphrodite/Venus
   D. Corinth synonymous with sexual immorality
   E. Paul preaches in synagogue, then turns
      to the Gentiles
   F. Jesus reassures St. Paul, "I will be with you"—
      Moses, Gideon, Jeremiah, Mary, etc.
   G. Paul stays two years

II. Ephesus (Acts 19)
   A. Temple to Artemis/Diana
   B. Known for occult practices
   C. Ephesus as headquarters to entire region
   D. God uses material objects to transmit grace
   E. Massive voluntary book-burning
   F. Riot; convert generosity vs. rioter greed
   G. Paul stays three years

III. What Do We Learn?
   A. St. Paul's zeal to go out; God is calling us
      to go out
   B. Welcoming those who come in, as if they
      were Christ himself

DISCUSS

4. How does Dr. Healy describe the cities of Corinth and Ephesus? How did the Jews receive St. Paul? What about the Gentiles?

_____

_____

5. What miracles did God work in Ephesus at the hands of St. Paul (see Acts 19:11-12)? How is Paul post-figuring Jesus?

_____

_____

6. Dr. Healy talks about a particular "zeal" of St. Paul. What was it? How did Cardinal Bergoglio demonstrate this zeal as the Archbishop of Argentina? What does Pope Francis call the Church to do today?

_____

_____

PART 3: ST. PAUL IN ROME
Watch the video teaching. The following is a brief outline of the topics covered.

I. St. Paul's Return to Jerusalem and Arrest
   A. Bound in the Spirit (obeying)   _____
   B. Gives testimony before Herod Agrippa
      in Caesarea (Acts 26)   _____
   C. Echoes Suffering Servant Songs (Isaiah 42:6-7)   _____
   D. Jesus doesn't preach to Gentiles before   _____
      his Death; but now he does through   _____
      his Body, the Church   _____
   E. Paul heads to Rome in chains,   _____
      not as he expected   _____

II. Rome (Acts 27-28)   _____
   A. Sails to Rome; shipwrecked in Malta   _____
   B. Preaches in Rome; lives there two years,   _____
      welcoming all, preaching with all boldness   _____

III. Why Does St. Luke End Here?   _____
   A. Freezes frame of story
   B. Paul bound, but not the word of God   _____
   C. Gospel on its way to the ends of the earth   _____

DISCUSS

7. What does the term "bound in the Spirit" (Acts 20:22) mean? And why do you think the author of Acts tell us that St. Paul was "bound in the Spirit" when he headed for Rome?

_____

_____

8. How is St. Paul able to say in Acts 26:22-23, "And so I stand here testifying both to small and great, saying nothing but what the prophets and Moses said would come to pass: that the Christ must suffer and that, by being the first to rise from the dead, he would proclaim light both to the people and to the Gentiles"?

_____

_____

9. St. Luke ends Acts with the following, "And he lived there two whole years at his own expense, and welcomed all who came to him, preaching the kingdom of God and teaching about the Lord Jesus Christ quite openly and unhindered" (Acts 28:30-31). Do you like this ending of Acts? Why or why not?

_____

_____

MEMORY VERSE

"He is not far from each one of us, for 'in him we live and move and have our being.'"

—**Acts 17:27-28**

CLOSING PRAYER

Lord God, in your great mercy,
you sent St. Paul out to seek the lost sheep.
Answering your call, he went out into the world
to share the saving message of Christ crucified.
Help us to prayerfully reflect on what his travels
mean for us as Christians today.
Like St. Paul,
may we have the courage to hold fast to the Gospel
without hesitation or compromise,
no matter the cost.
Grant us the humility to answer your call
to share the Gospel in our thoughts, words, and deeds,
always spreading the message of your mercy,
especially to those whose hearts dwell furthest from you.
We ask this through Christ our Lord.
Amen.

St. Paul, pray for us.

FURTHER READING

Catechism of the Catholic Church, 861-863

Pope Benedict XVI, *Saint Paul* **(Ignatius Press, 2009)**

Mitch Pacwa, *St. Paul: A Bible Study Guide for Catholics* **(Our Sunday Visitor, 2008)**

COMMIT—DAY 1
PETER AND PAUL: BROTHERS IN CHRIST

Despite their different backgrounds and experiences, Sts. Peter and Paul worked together to preach the Gospel and make disciples of Jesus Christ. Peter preached in Jerusalem at Pentecost and throughout Judea and Samaria; Paul made missionary journeys throughout the Greco-Roman world, traveling to Asia Minor, Macedonia, and Greece. Ultimately, these two Apostles ended up together in the capital city of Rome, where they were each martyred for their fidelity to their Lord.

Mosaic from facade of St. Paolo fuori le mura basilica. Christ the Teacher apostles Peter and Paul by Filippo Agricola and Nicola Consoni © Renata Sedmakova / shutterstock.com

Too often in modern times, these two great Apostles are seen as competitors rather than as brothers sharing in one mission—with non-Catholics taking St. Paul and Catholics taking St. Peter. Surprisingly, some turn to Scripture trying to promote such a division.

Read Galatians 2:11-14. What is St. Paul describing in this passage?

_____

_____

Read Acts 10:44–11:3. How might this previous encounter have influenced St. Peter to avoid eating with the Gentile Christians?

_____

_____

Read Acts 11:4-18 and Acts 15:5-11. What does St. Peter proclaim?

_____

_____

Growing up as a faithful Jew and living according to the Mosaic Law, St. Peter would not have eaten with uncircumcised men. But once God makes it clear that none of God's children are unclean, and that all who repent, Jew and Gentile alike, can receive the Spirit of God, Peter understands what St. Paul later writes—that the Mosaic ritual law was a only a temporary custodian over God's people until Christ came (Galatians 3:23-29). After baptizing Cornelius and his household, Peter stays at their house several days, which would have included eating numerous meals with these new Gentile converts to Christianity. Paul notes that Peter ate with the Gentiles at Antioch; it is only when Jewish Christians arrive at Antioch that Peter changes his behavior, perhaps remembering the criticism he previously had been subject to over this very issue. Peter wrongly chooses the road of least resistance.

Here God uses St. Paul to step into St. Peter's life and call him back to the narrow path. Paul was confounded that the arrival of Jewish Christians would prompt St. Peter to draw back from eating with uncircumcised Gentile Christians. Seeing Peter's error, and that his example was encouraging others to imitate this error, Paul rightly opposes Peter—not by disparaging his character or spreading rumors behind his back, but rather by confronting him as a brother, one on one, "to his face."

Far from being an example of division or antagonism between Sts. Peter and Paul, this episode shows the deepest level of brotherly affection between these two great saints. Look up the following verses. What aspect of filial friendship is highlighted?

Ecclesiastes 4:9-10 _____

Proverbs 18:19 _____

Proverbs 27:17 _____

Luke 17:3 _____

Icon of Apostles Saints Peter and Paul © Dmitry Kalinovsky / shutterstock.com

Sts. Peter and Paul were the truest of brothers in Christ. They shared one mission, proclaiming Jesus Christ to all who would listen, Jew and Gentile, circumcised and uncircumcised. And when one fell or sinned, the other corrected him so that each would walk in righteousness along the narrow path of Christ. If they were competitors, it was not against each other. Rather they competed together, united on the same team, competing for the crown of great glory that they both received when they laid down their lives.

This is why the Church, particularly in Rome, has understood that while it has St. Peter as its head and the Apostles as her foundation, its witness to Jesus Christ is modeled in a special way by the blood of Sts. Peter and Paul shed at their martyrdom in the capital city of the empire whose boundaries stretched to the ends of the earth. These two saints share one feast day, the feast of Sts. Peter and Paul on June 29th. The image of their two faces was the imprint used by the Church to seal her documents and declarations (bulls). Their apostolic prominence and unity is recalled in Christian art throughout the centuries, where these two men typically stand closest to Jesus, one on either side.

In our own lives, as we strive to live in imitation of Jesus Christ, it is an incredible blessing to have such a brother or sister, like Sts. Peter and Paul were to each other, whom we can trust to hold us accountable; one from whom we are willing to humbly receive difficult words of correction so that we might remain faithful to Christ. Is there someone with whom you might share this type of Christian friendship?

Several times in Scripture, St. Luke emphasizes the guidance of the Holy Spirit for St. Paul's missionary work:

> *"While they were worshiping the Lord and fasting, the Holy Spirit said, 'Set apart for me Barnabas and Saul for the work to which I have called them.'"*
> —Acts 13:2

Saint Paul paint from Paris - St. Severin church © Renata Sedmakova / shutterstock.com

> *"And they went through the region of Phrygia and Galatia, having been forbidden by the Holy Spirit to speak the word in Asia. And when they had come opposite Mysia, they attempted to go into Bithynia, but the Spirit of Jesus did not allow them."*
> —Acts 16:6-7

> *"And a vision appeared to Paul in the night: a man of Macedonia was standing beseeching him and saying, 'Come over to Macedonia and help us.' And when he had seen the vision, immediately we sought to go on into Macedonia, concluding that God had called us to preach the gospel to them."*
> —Acts 16:9-10

Even though the Spirit's intervention and direction during St. Paul's missionary journeys witnesses to Jesus' promise to be with his Apostles always, God sends him additional reassurance that he is not alone, no matter what happens next. Read Acts 18:5-11. What happens in this passage?

_____

_____

We read of the assurance of God's protection and presence many times in Sacred Scripture. Review the following promises:

To Isaac: "And the Lord appeared to him the same night and said, 'I am the God of Abraham your father; fear not, for I am with you and will bless you and multiply your descendants for my servant Abraham's sake'" (Genesis 26:24).

To Jacob: "Behold, I am with you and will keep you wherever you go, and will bring you back to this land; for I will not leave you until I have done that which I have spoken to you" (Genesis 28:15).

To Moses: "He said, 'But I will be with you; and this shall be the sign for you, that I have sent you: when you have brought forth the people out of Egypt, you shall serve God upon this mountain'" (Exodus 3:12).

To Gideon: "And the angel of the LORD appeared to him and said to him, 'The LORD is with you, you mighty man of valor'" (Judges 6:12).

To Jeremiah: "Be not afraid of them, for I am with you to deliver you, says the LORD" (Jeremiah 1:8).

To Mary: "And he came to her and said, 'Hail, full of grace, the Lord is with you!' But she was greatly troubled at the saying, and considered in her mind what sort of greeting this might be. And the angel said to her, 'Do not be afraid, Mary, for you have found favor with God'" (Luke 1:28-30).

Throughout history, God has made a point of expressing his personal care and concern for his people. His greatest desire has always been to be with them, to dwell among them, to share with them his very self. And just as he did with the patriarchs and prophets of old, he has promised to be with us until the end of the age (Matthew 28:20). In Baptism we have been adopted into the family of God, we are God's own children, and we can come to know him who is "Emmanuel... God with us" (Matthew 1:23).

God is not a distant entity, as was believed by the Epicureans that St. Paul encountered in Athens. He is not an "unknown god" (Acts 17:23). He is a personal God, who wants to be known by each and every person he has created. He is a loving Father who promises to be with us through good times and bad. St. Paul knew God's personal love, from his conversion, from the Scriptures, from the direction he received during his missionary journeys. This is the God he shared with Jews and Gentiles 2,000 years ago, and it is the same God we are called to share with all those who seek him today.

Spend some time today reflecting on how you would respond to someone who asked you, "Why do you believe in God?" Focus your response on sharing about your personal relationship with God, the God who is "with you" in your daily life, and inviting this other person to seek after God, who wants to be with them also.

_____

_____

Creation of Adam. Detail of the Sistine ceiling / Scala / Art Resource, NY

Commit—Day 3
St. Paul Writes to Those He Evangelized

After his preaching brought many to faith and Baptism in Jesus Christ, St. Paul continued to look after these new Christian communities, writing letters to them and visiting them on subsequent mission journeys. As Dr. Healy describes, Paul spent three years in Ephesus and knew that community very well. Let's look at the opening lines he writes to those who had become his brothers and sisters in the Faith.

> **LECTIO:** The practice of praying with Scripture, *lectio divina*, begins with an active and close reading of the Scripture passage. Read the Scripture passage below and then answer the questions to take a closer look at some of the details of the passage.

"[God the Father] destined us in love to be his sons through Jesus Christ, according to the purpose of his will, to the praise of his glorious grace which he freely bestowed on us in the Beloved. In him we have redemption through his blood, the forgiveness of our trespasses, according to the riches of his grace which he lavished upon us. For he has made known to us in all wisdom and insight the mystery of his will, according to his purpose which he set forth in Christ as a plan for the fulness of time, to unite all things in him, things in heaven and things on earth. In him, according to the purpose of him who accomplishes all things according to the counsel of his will, we who first hoped in Christ have been destined and appointed to live for the praise of his glory. In him you also, who have heard the word of truth, the gospel of your salvation, and have believed in him, were sealed with the promised Holy Spirit, who is the guarantee of our inheritance until we acquire possession of it, to the praise of his glory."

—Ephesians 1:5-14

According to St. Paul, who "destined us in love"?

_____

Who redeemed us through his blood?

_____

Who is the guarantee of our inheritance?

_____

Give some examples of vivid words (nouns, verbs, adjectives) and phrases St. Paul uses in this passage.

_____

> **MEDITATIO:** *Lectio*, a close reading and rereading, is followed by *meditatio*, time to reflect on the Scripture passage and to ponder the reason for particular events, descriptions, details, phrases, and even echoes from other Scripture passages that were noticed during *lectio*. Take some time now to meditate on the Scripture passage from page 185.

The following meditation is taking from a General Audience homily of Pope St. John Paul II on the opening verses of the Letter to the Ephesians, in which he recalls the words of St. John Chrysostom.

> *"In his First Homily on the Letter to the Ephesians, commenting on this Canticle, [St. John Chrysostom] reflects with gratitude on the 'blessings' with which we have been blessed 'in Christ': 'Indeed, what do you lack? You have become immortal, you have become free persons, you have become sons, you have become righteous, you have become brothers, coheirs who reign with him and with him you are glorified. All this has been given to us and, as it is written, '...will he not also give us all things with him?' (Rom 8:32). Your first fruit (cf. I Corinthians 15:20, 23) is adored by angels, cherubim and seraphim: so what could you possibly lack?' (PG 62, 11). ...What does this mean? It means that God passionately desires and ardently longs for our salvation. 'And why does he love us like this? Why does he feel such great affection for us? Out of goodness alone...not only did God free us from sin, but he also made us lovable...: he adorned our soul and made it beautiful, desirable and lovable.'"*
> —Pope St. John Paul II, General Audience, February 18, 2004

In *lectio* we saw that "God, the Father" destined us in love; we have redemption through the blood of the "Beloved" (Jesus Christ); and the "Holy Spirit" is the guarantee of our inheritance. Why do you think St. Paul organizes this passage around the Blessed Trinity? Do we know the work of the Trinity in our own life?

_____

_____

_____

Later in his letter, St. Paul will mention his imprisonment, he will exhort the Ephesians to continue in their fidelity to Christ and their unity with each other, he will give direction on family life, and he will make use of the armor of God to stay strong. But here in these opening verses, he simply rejoices in what he shares with the Ephesians—life in Christ. And this life is so wonder-full that St. Paul can't help using words like "destined us in love," "glorious grace," "riches of his grace," "freely bestowed," "beloved," and "lavished." When we think of our own life in Christ, do we have this same joy? Why is our witness of our joy in Christ important for evangelization?

_____

_____

_____

In our meditation passage, Pope St. John Paul II recalls how St. John Chrysostom reads these verses of joy and asks, "What could you possibly lack?" This seems to be St. Paul's exact thought. Even though he is a prisoner in chains (Ephesians 3:1, 4:1) when he writes his Letter to the Ephesians, he can't help but sing God's praises. What does Paul keep his focus on? What can we learn from him to help us retain joy in the midst of suffering?

_____

_____

_____

> **ORATIO, CONTEMPLATIO, RESOLUTIO:** Having read and meditated on today's Scripture passage, take some time to bring your thoughts to God (*oratio*) and engage God in silence (*contemplatio*). Then end your prayer by making a simple concrete resolution (*resolutio*) to respond to God's prompting of your heart in today's prayer.

_____

_____

_____

The Adoration of the Trinity / Erich Lessing / Art Resource, NY

COMMIT—DAY 4
SUFFERING SERVANT

"I rejoice in my sufferings for your sake." —Colossians 1:24

Jesus on the cross; created by the baroque painter Anthon Van Dyck © jorisvo / shutterstock.com

The prophet Isaiah prophesies of a "servant of the Lord" whom God will delight in and put his Spirit upon; who will bring back Jacob and Israel and be a light to the nations; who will open the eyes of the blind and bring release to prisoners; who will have a sharp tongue that will teach...but who will also suffer and give his back to the smiters; who will be despised, rejected, oppressed, afflicted, wounded for our transgressions, and bruised for our iniquities; and whose grave would be with the wicked and the rich man though he had done no wrong (Isaiah 42:1-7; 49:1-6; 50:4-9; 52:14–53:12).

Jesus Christ is clearly the fulfillment of Isaiah's prophecies. Just as these, and all the Old Testament prophecies, pointed forward to Christ, in a similar way, the lives of the Apostles and of every baptized Christian throughout the ages should be an imitation of Christ, pointing back to our Redeemer and Lord. This being true, it shouldn't surprise us to find that St. Paul sees himself as another "suffering servant," following in the footsteps and imitating "the" Suffering Servant, Jesus Christ.

Look up the following verses. How is St. Paul a suffering servant like Jesus Christ?

Acts 13:44-48 _____

Ephesians 3:1 _____

2 Corinthians 11:23-27 _____

St. Paul recognizes that as Christ's servant, he will be called to live and to die like Christ, as he says to the Philippians, "For to me to live is Christ, and to die is gain" (Philippians 1:21). Paul not only recognizes this truth but rejoices in such suffering, confident in God's promise that he will be victorious in the end. He also exhorts us, "Be imitators of me, as I am of Christ" (1 Corinthians 11:1).

In this session we looked at St. Paul's evangelical efforts throughout much of the Greco-Roman world. Over the sessions of this entire study, we have looked at numerous Apostles and disciples and how they sought to go out to the lost sheep, finding those steeped in the mire of intellectualism, materialism, and sexual immorality, and offering them hope through the message of the Gospel. They encountered plenty of skepticism and rejection, but their personal witness to the love of God and the freedom from sin in Jesus Christ brought many to faith. By God's grace and the tireless efforts of the first Christians, the Church spread from a tiny little land in the Middle East to the ends of the earth, just as Christ had prophesied.

Like Sts. Peter and Paul and the first Christians, we are all called to evangelize, to "always be prepared to make a defense to any one who calls you to account for the hope that is in you, yet do it with gentleness and reverence" (1 Peter 3:15). We are all called to imitate Jesus, the Suffering Servant, and to be a light to the nations. At times this will mean having that "tongue that will teach," answering a question about the faith and our life, defending Christ and the Christian worldview, teaching our children, etc. It will always mean living a life filled with works of mercy, sharing our goods with the poor, caring for a sick neighbor or child, helping another in need, etc. Often it is our life, our willingness to suffer for others, that will win us the opportunity to speak of Jesus Christ.

We close this Commit Day by looking at a modern-day suffering servant, Elisabeth Leseur, who imitated St. Paul and Jesus, and whose willingness to suffer for others eventually won the conversion of her husband to faith in Jesus Christ. Here is her story:

When Elisabeth married Felix Leseur in 1889 after a brief engagement, she was a common Catholic woman—not particularly devout. Though her husband was "profoundly anti-religious," a prominent intellectual atheist who even published a well-known atheist newspaper, he promised that he would not try to destroy her faith. And yet he stockpiled atheist literature and encouraged her to read it. He dismissed her faith as ridiculous and did his best to teach her the foolishness of her ways.

Rather than recoil from his efforts, Elisabeth quietly began to build up her own library of Catholic works in order to solidify her faith. She took time each day to meditate on Scripture and began to practice the sacraments regularly. Understanding that her own preaching would not win over her husband to Christ, Elisabeth developed an interior life full of prayer and sacrifice, knowing that the Holy Spirit is responsible for the salvation of souls, as she wrote in her journal:

> *"It is not in arguing or in lecturing that I can make them know what God is to the human soul. But in struggling with myself, in becoming, with His help, more Christian and more valiant, I will bear witness to Him whose humble disciple I am."*

> *"O my God, it is indeed true that Thou alone canst make certain things understood; all the arguments in the world are nothing to Thy sovereign voice in the depths of the soul. Thou alone canst penetrate the depths and reach the mysterious place in the soul where great transformations occur."*

Rather than argue, Elisabeth found another way:

> *"This is, in fact, my task: to do my different duties without anyone's suspecting what trouble I have in reconciling them, to forget myself, to develop what God has given me of reason and intelligence, to banish pride even in the most subtle forms I know so well, to love strongly without self-seeking, to accept by divine grace the duty of every day and hour and never to neglect it, however small it may be. I shall often fall, but that help from above for which I shall humbly petition daily will not fail me. Besides, to live is to fight, to suffer, and to love."*

Upon her death, after years of sacrifice and prayers, Elisabeth's husband not only converted but became a Dominican priest. In an introduction to her diary, her husband describes her life's mission beautifully:

> *"My beloved wife, Elisabeth, prayed incessantly for my return to the Faith...; day by day for this intention did she accept and offer up all her privations, sacrifices, trials, sufferings, and at the end, even her death."*
>
> —*The Secret Diary of Elisabeth Leseur*, p. xiii

Her cause is up for canonization at this time. *The Secret Diary of Elisabeth Leseur* is full of insight into the interior and exterior life of a modern-day, suffering servant and silent evangelist.

Prayerfully consider how you might be called to become a suffering servant. List three ways that you can offer your suffering or sacrifices in your daily life for the salvation of a loved one.

1. _____

_____

2. _____

_____

3. _____

_____

COMMIT—DAY 5
TRUTH AND BEAUTY

Christ Enthroned and the Apostles in the Heavenly Jerusalem,
c. 410-417, Church of Santa Pudentiana, Rome, Italy

Christ Enthroned and the Apostles in the Heavenly Jerusalem / Scala / Art Resource, NY

Today we step back in time to the ancient Roman neighborhood on the Viminal Hill. Where once stood fashionable villas, we now find the ancient church of Santa Pudentiana, built, according to legend, over the former residence of the Christian Senator Pudens, who offered hospitality to St. Peter and is named in 2 Timothy 4:21. At the early house church that met in this home, St. Peter shared the Gospel and celebrated the Eucharist with a growing Christian community. Here St. Peter ordained his three immediate papal successors, Sts. Linus, Cletus, and Clement.

Among the oldest mosaics in Rome, Santa Pudentiana's apse mosaic is famous for its beauty, naturalism, and composition. Created only a century after Constantine and Licinius's decree giving Christianity legal status, this mosaic portrays Christianity's expanding triumph over the pagan understanding of the cosmos. Jesus Christ replaces Jupiter, king of the gods in the ancient Roman religion. Jesus, like Jupiter, is bearded with long hair, wearing a rich robe, and is seated on a bejeweled throne on a plush cushion. Instead of holding Jupiter's thunderbolt of power, Jesus raises his right hand, not in a show of might, but in blessing. In his left hand Jesus holds a book inscribed *Dominus Conservator Ecclesiae Pudentiana,* "The Lord, Preserver of the Church of Pudentiana."

On either side of Jesus, we find ten Apostles, seated in a beautifully colonnaded courtyard (during a renovation in the sixteenth century, the images of the two Apostles on either end were destroyed). The artist portrays the Apostles, dressed in their distinctive single-striped togas, as Roman senators. But instead of the power of temporal governance possessed by the Roman senate, Jesus has invested the Apostles with the power to "bind and loose," the teaching, governing, and sanctifying office of the Church (CCC 873).

Seated on Jesus' immediate right and left are the illustrious Sts. Peter and Paul, whose iconography in Christian art was fixed by the second or third century. St. Peter is consistently rendered with gray curly hair, a short beard, and a stocky build. St. Paul is portrayed with a receding hairline, brown hair, and a longer, pointy beard. From the earliest times, Christians saw Sts. Peter and Paul as the new founders of Christian Rome, taking the place of Romulus and Remus, ancient Rome's founders. These pagan twin brothers avenged themselves over a ruthless king who attempted to take their lives and prevent them from taking the throne of their grandfather. Sts. Peter and Paul, in a parallel story, are martyred on either side of the Tiber River by the ruthless ruler, Nero, in an attempt to prevent Christianity's spread. The artist shows us Nero's failed attempt, as Jesus, not Nero or Jupiter, reigns with his Apostles as he had promised: "Truly, I say to you, in the new world, when the Son of man shall sit on his glorious throne, you who have followed me will also sit on twelve thrones, judging the twelve tribes of Israel" (Matthew 19:28).

One ancient tradition tells of Sts. Peter and Paul's martyrdom on the same day, with their subsequent feast day celebrated together on the day of their martyrdom. Just as in the Church's liturgy, Christian art also celebrated its two founders by almost always depicting Peter and Paul together, often flanking Jesus on either side as we see in the apse mosaic in Santa Pudentiana. Their position declares to the viewer their importance in Christ's plan to bring the gospel message to then ends of the earth: Peter, apostle to the Jews, and Paul, apostle to the Gentiles (Galatians 2:7-8). As St. Leo the Great so beautifully described in a homily for Peter and Paul's feast during his pontificate in the fifth century: "For these are the men, through whom the light of Christ's gospel shone on you, O Rome, and through whom you, who was the teacher of error, were made the disciple of Truth" (Leo the Great, Sermon 82.1).

Christ Enthroned and the Apostles in the Heavenly Jerusalem / Scala / Art Resource, NY

Directly behind both Sts. Peter and Paul, a woman holds out a wreath to crown each Apostle. In ancient times, wreaths were signs of victory, awarded to those victorious in athletic competitions, as well as to commanders victorious in battle. Look up the following verses. How do Paul and Peter speak of obtaining an "unfading crown of glory"?

1 Corinthians 9:24-27 _____

_____

1 Peter 5:4 _____

_____

Behind Jesus, a glorious gold, jeweled cross stands on the hill of Calvary. What was an instrument of torture, shame, and death in pagan Rome, Jesus Christ made into the means of salvation when he offered himself in love on the Cross. As they prepared for their own martyrdom, many Roman Christians likely kept before their eyes their Lord, who "endured the cross, despising the shame, and is seated at the right hand of the throne of God" (Hebrews 12:2), trusting in God's grace that they might share in Christ's victory and receive a crown like Sts. Peter and Paul before them, as St. Pudentiana's apse mosaic shows and as this ancient hymn describes:

Christ Enthroned and the Apostles in the Heavenly Jerusalem / Scala / Art Resource, NY

The teacher of the world and keeper of heaven's gate,
Rome's founders twain and rulers too of every land,
Triumphant over death by sword and shameful cross,
With laurel crowned are gathered to the eternal band.

—*Decora Lux*, fifth-century hymn to Sts. Peter and Paul

This apse mosaic in the church of Santa Pudentiana represented the new founding of Rome as a Christian city, a city of God. The old Rome, ruled by Jupiter, founded by Romulus and Remus, and governed by the senate and people of Rome, is reimagined as the new Christian Rome, the city of God, presided over by the Just Judge, Jesus Christ, flanked by those he sent to be its founders, Sts. Peter and Paul, and taught, governed, and sanctified by his holy Apostles, a city in which the early Christians worked to create a civilization of love by spreading the Gospel of Jesus Christ. This was the vision presented to the Romans worshipping in this church as they beheld this beautiful mosaic. Just as the Apostles and martyrs had persevered and emerged victorious from the persecutions of pagan Rome, so too each Christian worshipper was reminded that as they persevered and fought the good fight, they too could look forward to finishing the race victorious and receiving the imperishable crown of righteousness (2 Timothy 4:7-8).

Take a moment to journal your ideas, questions, or insights about this lesson. Write down thoughts you had that may not have been mentioned in the text or the discussion questions. List any personal applications you got from the lessons. What challenged you the most in the teachings? How might you turn what you've learned into specific action?

_____

_____

_____

_____

_____

_____

_____

_____

_____

_____

_____

_____

_____

_____

_____

_____

_____

_____